the fun
starts here

drawing by Natacha Ledwidge

the fun starts here

A practical guide
to the bliss of babies

PAULA YATES

BLOOMSBURY

First published 1990

Copyright © 1990 by Paula Yates

The moral right of the author has been asserted

Bloomsbury Publishing Ltd, 2 Soho Square, London W1V 5DE

A CIP catalogue record for this book
is available from the British Library

'I've Got You Under My Skin',
(Cole Porter) © Chappell Co. Inc.
reproduced by permission of Warner Chappell Music Ltd

ISBN 0 7475 0765 1

10 9 8 7 6 5 4 3 2 1

Typeset by Rowland Phototypesetting Ltd,
Bury St Edmunds, Suffolk

Printed by Butler and Tanner Ltd,
Frome and London

Photographs pages 1 and 2 of plate section
© Brian Aris
All other photographs © Ruf Tuf Productions 1990
and not to be reproduced without permission

Everyone knows God couldn't send angels to earth so he sent mothers instead, but are we in danger of treating mothers as second-class citizens who do nothing much all day but wash bottoms and bottle gooseberries for the local WI? Are our children becoming leisure-time activities? Media pressure makes many women feel they will turn into vegetables if they give up full-time work and put their children first. Magazines conjure up images of women who deftly juggle being sexy sirens, nuclear physicists and high-powered executives with having ten minutes left at the end of the day for some 'quality time' with their babies. But maybe the truth is that these women are simply juggling between feeling guilty and feeling shattered.

The Fun Starts Here is a celebration of the experience of having a baby around the house, and gives much useful and encouraging advice to new mothers on how they can go about restructuring their lives around their new children. It is also a practical guide to everything from home nappy-rash cures to pain relief during labour to massage techniques for babies, beginning with conception and ending with the baby's first birthday. The book is a very personal view of motherhood, emphasising the good things: the bliss of babies.

To Bob, Fifi and Peaches, and the next gorgeous
Geldof girl

Contents

I've got you under my skin
I've got you deep in the heart of me
So deep, so deep
That you are a part of me
I've got you under my skin

But why should I try to resist
When baby I know so well
I've got you under my skin?

—'I've Got You Under My Skin',
Cole Porter

INTRODUCTION

I come from a long line of mothers – and they haven't always shared the same ideas. The first one in the family that I can remember is my mother's mother. During the war, when my own mother was just a teeny baby, the merest hum of a doodlebug in the far distance was enough to make her lunge out into the back garden where she would play her cornet loudly up at the skies to frighten the enemy off.

She then became rather glamorous within the family because she inherited a vast fortune from a man who had something to do with the invention of the Teasmade. She fitted out her home in wildly swirling purple-and-pink floral carpets and a huge wardrobe. I remember the costumes vividly – she bought lots and lots of multi-coloured lamé catsuits with very large flares and matching ponchos. Then my granny embarked on an almost permanent around-the-world cruise on the *QE2*, where her days were filled with dancing the rumba and playing her cornet on the first-class poop deck.

Then there was my father's mother. My father married my mother when he was middle aged and she was just out of her teens, and my grandmother must have been about three hundred and eight by then. My mother seems to feel that the marriage was doomed from the very start, mainly because my father insisted on holding hands with his mother in all the wedding photographs.

Which brings me to my own mother. Who was glamour personified. She went off to Rome and became a starlet in Fellini films. This intriguing career was embarked on after Fellini threw a live cockroach down the front of her swimsuit by way of introduction. She then accidentally knocked him out, delivering a swift left-hook that toppled him on to the patent-leather sun swing near by, whereupon a large pina colada had to be flung at his face to revive him.

After this tumult, he invited her out to dinner. Throughout the meal she was aware of the eyes of every diner on her alone. It wasn't until her dessert that she glanced down to notice that the underwiring from her supremely cantilevered bra had popped out and was entangled in her necklace a couple of inches under her chin . . .

Sadly, I was not around for much of my mother's early working life. She was one of the new breed of Sixties mothers – the ones who believed that children were just little adults. She often noted that children were happy if their parents were. This is an idea about mothering that I still subscribe to – but it only makes sense if the child is actually with her mother while she is being happy.

When I was little I lived in a massive mansion with endless grounds on the side of a mountain in deepest Wales. My father suffered from deep depression and my grandmother, who was supposed to be looking after me, was not cut out for the daily machinations of bringing up a small child. Life was Gothic, to put it mildly, but I had one retreat.

In our garden, there was an old cottage once used by the thirty-six gardeners employed to keep the strimmer on the topiary. Now the cottage was filled, floor to ceiling, room by room, with every single edition of the *Saturday Evening Post*, America's favourite family magazine. My father had accidentally bought them all with a pulpit when under the impression that he was bidding for an avocado bathroom suite. At the time my father had a passion for bathroom suites and we were one of the few families ever with an ensuite library and bathroom. But the magazines (especially the Fifties ones) became the foundation of a lifetime's dreams. Here, I thought, was reality. This was what everyone else's family was like. Real families had mothers with pristine white aprons who were always there, and baked things for sons with crewcuts and daughters with anklesocks. Here were mothers who waited happily at home for their husbands to jump over the white picket fence, back from work, laughing and smiling, not mothers who turned up occasionally at the school play with jewels in their navels.

This is what inspired me to write a book that was not only a practical guide (in the sense that it delved deep into nappies, bottoms, piles and labour) but was also a note of encouragement to any woman trying to decide whether giving up work and staying at home with her baby was a good idea. It's a marvellous idea, and this is a book about mothering which is positive, a kind of celebration of having a family and of the bliss of babies.

As I write, my main difficulty is getting my stomach behind the Olivetti, as I'm just about to have my third baby. Writing about babies and pregnancy while pregnant, I know very well the tumult of emotions pregnancy can inspire. Some days I would wake and gaze out of the window seeing trees that were like emeralds, the bluest skies imaginable, and I would sit at the typewriter convinced that I had been

Rupert Brooke's vest in a past life. On other days I would catch a glimpse of my fat gut, spot yet another pair of Fifi's knickers on a doorknob and come downstairs to be greeted with a teetering pile of dog diarrhoea or washing-up and spend the rest of the day gazing into space wondering if I would ever be able to write another enthusiastic word about families, and pondering why my husband hadn't left me for a topless go-go dancer from Skegness.

I have to admit that I also wrote the book because I wanted an opportunity to have a mammoth boast about my two daughters, Fifi and Peaches, although I believe certain passages where I claimed that they were both able to speak fluent Swahili and bake a soufflé at the age of one have been deleted. Certainly, being able to be at home with the two of them, watching them get more delicious every day, has been the greatest push I needed to my desk.

But what of my mater? I hear you ask. Well, one of my last memories of childhood is my mother arriving in a vision of red and leopardskin at the boarding school I was attending eight miles from our home. She grabbed me out of school, explaining to the bewildered head-mistress that I had an urgent audience with the Pope, which I've always felt was a slightly excessive excuse to use for leaving school three days before the end of term – but it worked.

We swept off to the local John Menzies. My mother had by now become a writer, and her first novel was being much lauded. We were on our way to buy the *Sunday Times* which that day was running a large review of the book. As she dramatically swept past the queue and opened the paper, it became apparent why the review was so large – the picture of the author covered about three acres. The literary editor had deemed it appropriate to run an old film still of my mum, wearing a corset and suspenders, and wielding a whip at the photographer as though he were a lamb chop for lunch. My mother leaned wearily back against three old issues of *Gardener's World*. 'They'd never have done this to bloody A. J. P. Taylor,' she hissed at me, slapping the paper shut and sweeping out again . . .

So although life with her could never be called boring, it all made me feel that I had to attempt to alter things radically. Perhaps when my children are grown-up they'll think I went too far the other way; they'll probably regard me as mothering's answer to the reinforced liberty bodice. It won't be until my daughters have children that a perfect balance will be struck – I'm sure they'll manage to get it right!

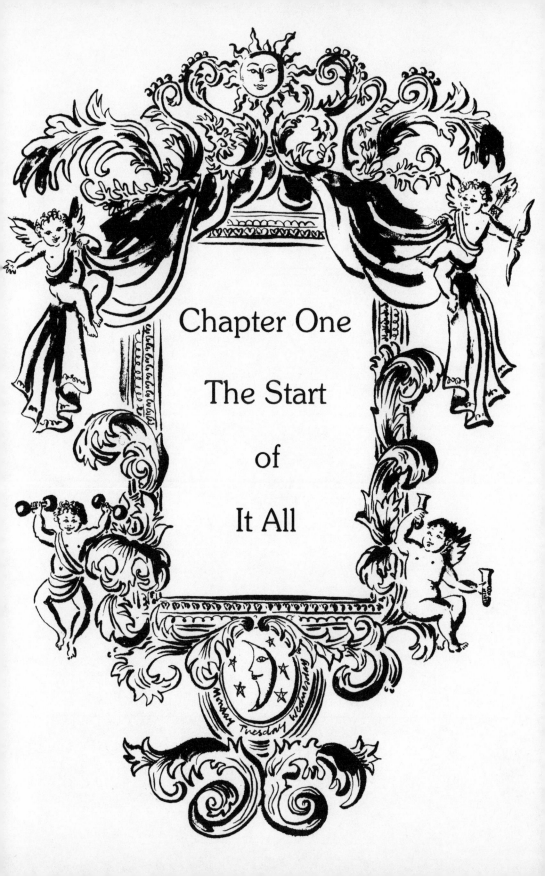

Chapter One

The Start

of

It All

It's hard to know when the time is right to have a baby. Pregnancy often happens just as you're re-building the toilet, about to be promoted to Big Enchilada, or going up the Amazon on a raft. However, with improved contraception and today's lack of pressure to marry early, it seems wildly sensible to wait until you both really long for a baby. A wanted baby will be happy, secure, and loved, and this will have a huge impact on how she brings up her own children.

Having a baby changes you far more than you could possibly imagine. When I was first pregnant at twenty-two with Fifi, I had no experience whatsoever to prepare me for the impact she would make. I didn't have a huge extended family, and had never even held a baby before. I had no inkling of the passionate love affair that was to develop between us – or of how completely I was to reorganise my life around it. I remember being completely dumbfounded by a disposable nappy, and utterly besotted by this fat little creature who acted like she belonged to us. I didn't know any nursery rhymes to sing to Fifi when I held her in my arms so I used to launch into impassioned versions of 'I've Got You Under My Skin' and 'It Happened in Monterey', both of which she could sing with aplomb at eighteen months old. And in retrospect, the songs Frank crooned to Ava couldn't have been more suitable, as I threw myself into my big love affair with her.

Feeling halfhearted about babies – or regarding them as a leisure-time activity to be fitted in between the 'real' business of life, work, is a bad way to start off. You'll find that juggling your life can't be done with the ease that is portrayed in the media. Every time I slump on to the sofa in front of the television, I seem to be greeted by women in Frederick's of Hollywood mink-trimmed split-crotch knickers, holding a portaphone in one hand, a baby and the *Financial Times* in the other. She is a lover, worker, mother, and nuclear astro-physicist, the voice-over tells me, as I tuck into my fourteenth Battenburg fancy.

THE START OF IT ALL

What the voice-over fails to mention is that she is also knackered and guilty, and that her baby would love to be with *her* more than anyone else in the world.

HOW TO MAKE SURE YOU'RE IN PEAK PHYSICAL CONDITION FOR PREGNANCY

Many people don't think about their health until after they discover they're pregnant. But if you have made a concrete decision to become pregnant, it's never too soon to get a head start on good health habits. The following health checks are a good idea.

Make a date with your dentist (not at the local Roxy) Unless you've always gone every six months you should see your dentist at least once *before* trying to get pregnant. The main reason for this is that X-rays can be harmful to the foetus. Once you discover you're pregnant, all X-rays should be avoided, especially during the earliest weeks of development when the baby's cells are rapidly growing and are ultra-sensitive to radiation. If you need X-rays, and you suspect you are already pregnant, it's best to postpone them until you know it's safe. Pregnancy may trigger tooth and gum problems, especially in the later months as hormonal changes affect your body's immunity and lower your defences against plaque.

Your Rubella (German measles) vaccine If you're not immune to this disease, which can cause miscarriages and also birth defects, a simple blood test will tell you. Try to have this six months ahead. If you do have to have the jab, try not to get pregnant for three months afterwards. If you're already pregnant or think there's a chance you may be, don't get innoculated as the vaccine may harm the baby. If you are pregnant and become exposed to German measles, a gamma-globulin shot can protect you and your unborn baby from the disease.

Don't let the Pill and IUD cause problems The standard gynaecologist's advice about coming off the Pill is to try to wait two natural periods before trying to conceive (although I don't know anyone who can bear to wait, once they've made the decision – but I am just telling you the good advice!). IUD users can also avoid worries by following similar guidelines.

Better-before-than-after tests If you've the slightest suspicion that you or your partner are from birth-defect-risk families, with close links to Down's syndrome or mental retardation, or if you come from any ethnic group which could be exposed to other risks – for example, if you're black, sickle cell disease, or, if you have Central European roots, the fatal Tay-Sachs' disease – you should both schedule genetic check-ups at your local hospital. There are two reasons for this: some of the tests are easier to do when you're not pregnant; and knowing the risks beforehand, being aware of what you and your child would have to face if the odds were against you, will make it easier to face any tough decisions you might have ahead of you.

Get used to your doctor It's obvious that it will be a great deal easier to have a confident birth which goes according to your own personal wishes if the doctor delivering your baby is someone with whom you have developed a 'relationship'. Unfortunately, in the NHS this rarely seems possible.

Do you need to diet? If you are underweight, anaemic or a touch on the porky side, now is the time to balance your eating habits – *not* the minute you find out you're pregnant. Give yourself six months to start building good eating habits and trying to break bad ones. Good nutrition builds a healthier baby. Here are some of the things you should start trying to build into your diet: if you are on the Pill, your body's reserves of the vitamin B6, which is a key nutrient for baby development, could already be very low. IUDs are another nutrient drainer because of the longer, heavier periods you may have had which could have been robbing you of iron. An iron supplement will help and so will a diet rich in iron and B6-providing foods, like meat, especially liver, fish, poultry, leafy green vegetables, beans, wholegrain breads and cereals. You should also take a morning multi-vitamin.

Being overweight or underweight can cause complications in pregnancy. Mothers-to-be who are overweight find themselves more susceptible to diabetes and high blood pressure. They can also give birth to overweight babies, who may look cute but who will be unhealthy. But pregnancy is not the time to start living on two lettuce leaves a day. Underweight mothers are prone to have underweight babies. If you need to gain, doctors advise you to make every effort to gain the weight *before* you get pregnant, otherwise you'll have to gain all the extra weight during your pregnancy.

Start to fight those piles now! Constipation and piles plague many women's pregnancies and are not just the stuff of schoolgirl jokes, although it is almost impossible to talk about them without giggling. Until you've got them. You can try and avoid them by eating more raw fruits and vegetables, dried fruits, wholegrain breads and cereals. Making fibre a regular part of your diet will save you much discomfort later.

Drinks All things in moderation as you build up towards your pregnancy. For example, a normal dose of vitamins may be helpful, whereas a mega-dose might be harmful. The same applies to all drinks: normal coffee, tea and Cola drinking is OK, but four or more cups a day could easily be caffeine-risky. Nobody really knows the long-term effects of that. Besides, if you're trying to get pregnant, it's a good idea to cut out caffeine altogether, because doctors have discovered that it can halve your chances of getting pregnant.

Alcohol It's also a good idea to give up alcohol. Scientists recently discovered that giving up when you *are* pregnant is actually too late to prevent some of its side-effects harming the baby. Not only could alcohol be damaging the reproductive systems of thousands of women, it could also be putting them at risk of miscarriages and infertility, or of giving birth to babies with mental and physical handicaps. Professor Matthew Kaufman, a world expert on early embryology (and try saying that after a couple of Tequila Slammers) has shown that alcohol can damage eggs before conception as well as harm the growing baby. His research suggests that alcohol can reach the ovaries. The damage that results from this exposure, he believes, could be the cause of thousands of miscarriages suffered by British women every year. He emphasises that, although he believes that alcohol can damage the eggs at any time, a woman who binged as a teenager should not assume that she will have childbearing problems later, especially if she gives up alcohol when she wants to have a baby. However, the risks are particularly high among older women, that is, those over forty. Women differ so much in their ability to clear alcohol out of their systems that Professor Kaufman refuses to specify a safe level of drinking. A toxic level for one could be one drink, and for another it could be half a bottle a day. Better safe than sorry. Or hungover.

Smoking and drugs Smoking increases the odds that your baby will have below-normal birth weight, and some evidence suggests that this is true of marijuana use, too. Better to quit before you're pregnant, because it's harder to quit once you are – the extra stresses and demands put on you by your pregnancy and the changes in your life may make it difficult for you to give up bad habits. Also bear in mind that certain medications – both prescription and routine, over-the-counter pain and headache relievers – may be harmful to the baby. It is wise to check with your doctor before taking *anything* and to try to get into relaxation, exercise, yoga and meditation techniques to relieve you of headaches or minor pain.

TIMING IT RIGHT: CONCEPTION

When you are close to ovulation, the level of the luteinising hormone (LH) in the body rises sharply, signalling to the ovaries to release the egg. LH is present in your urine and the increased surge can be detected by testing a sample at the same time every day, around the middle of the menstrual cycle. From one to three days after the surge is detected, ovulation should follow, and as a sperm can survive for up to twenty-four hours in a woman's body, you can enhance your chances of making a baby by having intercourse as soon as you register the increase of hormone, and for the next three days. Although expensive, an ovulation kit is a good idea, especially if you have very irregular periods. Not all women ovulate every month, even though they may have some form of bleeding.

Ovulation Tests

The following kits are more efficient at detecting ovulation than the methods of taking your temperature or identifying changes in your cervical mucus. The kits stipulate on which day (and it is different in each case) to start testing – a calculation which is based on the length of the preceding menstrual cycle.

Ovustick This kit is available in a six- and nine-test size. The urine sample has to be taken between 10 a.m. and 8 p.m., and cups with lids are provided for storing it. As the test is in two, half-hour sections, you must wait an hour for the result. The white Ovustick turns blue when exposed to increased levels of LH. The colour change should be quite pronounced. This kit's instructions are easy to follow and it is simple to use.

Discretest This requires your first morning's urine, for which you must provide your own container. In our household, this inevitably turns out to be an empty 2 litre Dandelion & Burdock bottle. The test takes only thirty minutes. It involves no rinsing and little mess and the colour is checked against a window with three colour slides ranging from dark-purple to light-mauve. LH is indicated by the lighter shade.

Ovuquick This gives you six or nine tests. Supplied with this four-minute test-kit are cups for your urine, a selection of bottles, test pads in foil with their own labels, a plastic tube and a urine dropper. You take your sample from between 10 a.m. and 8 p.m. and should not use the first urine of the morning. Before you use the kit, you have to add liquid from the plastic tube to Bottle B and leave it to stand for ten minutes. You then remove a test pad from its foil and deposit on to it drops from urine and then drops from the four bottles in sequence. A blue reference spot will appear, to which you should match the test spot. If the test spot matches or is darker than the reference spot, you should ovulate within forty hours, although having done the test you may well be too exhausted to have sex.

Clearplan This is available from chemists in a ten-test pack. You collect your sample either first thing in the morning or late in the evening by holding the urine sampler in a stream of urine for five seconds. You should not have passed urine for four hours previously. The test takes half an hour and is divided into three ten-minute segments. When LH is present, the end of the sampler turns from white to blue and can be recorded on a colour-coded chart.

First Response This is available in either a three- or six-test pack. It uses the first urine of the morning. The test takes twenty minutes, divided into one fifteen-minute part and one five-minute part. A record chart is provided with the instructions, which are easy to understand. A colour change from clear to turquoise indicates a surge in your body of LH.

Why Trying Too Hard Doesn't Work

Some of you may be reading this book willing it to get you pregnant.

When baby fever grips, it is now believed that the stress it causes can actually affect your fertility. One fertility clinic is trying to counteract this anxiety through stress management courses, which sound like something for the boardroom but actually are designed for the bedroom! The Holly House Hospital in Essex and its medical directors have long felt that suffering the mammoth disappointment of not being

pregnant, month after month, is in itself an obstacle to conception.

Everybody has heard about people who tried and tried and tried for a baby, finally gave up and immediately found themselves pregnant quite spontaneously (well, *almost* spontaneously). Gynaecologist Dr Gowrie Motha, who runs Holly House's programme, tackles stress with a mixture of alternative or complementary therapies such as creative visualisation, reflexology, aromatherapy, as well as self-hypnosis and deep relaxation techniques. You can try many of these things at home – or seek out an alternative health centre near you. Health food shops often have books on these subjects – and include your partner, that way it's much more fun.

For many couples, life can become an unmerry-go-round of tests, pills, surgery and also a sex life geared to the clock and calendar. Anyone who has suffered from the problem of infertility will realise that it is a health problem unlike any other, because its dark tentacles reach out into every aspect of your life: your sense of self, your friendships (particularly where friends have children), and your marriage. Although many doctors dismiss the psychological factors, some – such as Dr Sherman Silber, the author of *How to Get Pregnant* – feel that emotions exert a powerful influence on every woman's reproductive system. Frequently, grief, upheavals in lifestyle, changes at work, or moving home can have an effect and disrupt the timing of ovulation – if not cause it to cease altogether.

Some doctors find that simply improving the timing of intercourse, and not leaping up immediately afterwards can do the trick. But it is this very emphasis on timing and technique that makes for more stress. Most doctors recommend that, in order to increase their chances of having a baby, couples should have sex on the two or three days preceding ovulation. Sadly, when making love becomes making babies, the ghost of one's gynaecologist looms up in the bedroom – often clutching a chart marked with Xs, denoting when sex is 'required'. These demands are especially hard on partners. It isn't easy to feel sexy to order. Some husbands have even discovered they have difficulty getting an erection – which is all you need! To survive sex on demand, it is best to try not to think of it as passionate lovemaking on a fur rug in front of the fire, but to regard those instances of sex as rather scientifically determined. Then, on the occasions when you're not ovulating, use the time to indulge yourselves and your fantasies.

Family, Friends and Infertility

Unaware of the misery and pressure that many infertile couples are experiencing, family and friends inevitably blunder on asking for information – if not an actual baby. The result of this is increased anger, depression and guilt. Friends can often, unintentionally, further upset the infertile couple by trying to suggest that they're really lucky not having children because of the trouble, expense and mess. Trying to minimise a mammoth problem by complaining about children is simply heartless and ungrateful.

To avoid outside interference, couples should explain gently that they'd rather not discuss it because they find it a painful topic. This should shut anyone up. If it doesn't, you should see less of the people for a while – at a time like this, couples need to be self-protective. The same advice applies to events that women who have been trying for a baby for some time find particularly torturous – baby showers (when friends collect to give each other stupid soft toys for an impending arrival), christenings, circumcisions, family-orientated holidays. Don't go if it's going to upset you.

The most emotionally charged issue for an infertile woman is how to deal with pregnant women, especially when they are friends or relatives. Some women find that they can't bear to see a pregnant woman and find it really depressing.

Unfortunately, some friendships won't survive the crisis of infertility – some friends won't understand your need to pull back in order to decrease pain and will take it personally.

The Chances of a Miracle

Here are the most widely available sources of help for infertile couples. It must be stressed that the overall success rate of treatment is still only about 30 per cent, and services vary widely according to region. Treatment is available both privately and with the NHS, but the first person to speak to is your GP. You may find, particularly if you are quite young, that you are told to go on trying on your own – but don't take no for an answer if you have been trying for more than a year.

Tubal surgery Surgeons are adept at unblocking clogged Fallopian tubes, which are the passageways releasing the eggs out of the ovaries.

After surgery, X-rays show an 80–90 per cent success rate. But the post-surgery odds of becoming pregnant are lower – at best 10–20 per cent for women who had infection damage, but up to 60 per cent for women who were having reversal of tubal sterilisation.

In-vitro fertilisation (IVF) This is suitable for women with damaged tubes which cannot be repaired. For women trying IVF, the egg and the sperm actually meet in a test tube, and forty-eight hours later the resulting embryo is implanted into the womb. This technique was pioneered in England by Patrick Steptoe and Bob Edwards and there are now thousands of children walking around – the living, happy results of successful treatment.

Gamete intra-Fallopian transfer (GIFT) For women with normal Fallopian tubes but who nevertheless have difficulty conceiving. Eggs are removed from a woman's ovary, mixed with sperm and immediately returned by surgery to the Fallopian tube to fertilise in a natural environment.

Artificial insemination by donor While other baby-making techniques aim at women's problems, donor sperm can sometimes come to the rescue if a man's sperm count is low. Artificial insemination using washed and concentrated semen from a woman's own husband is sometimes tried before using a donor, usually when a woman has an allergy to her husband's sperm.

Fertility drugs For women who don't ovulate, or ovulate irregularly, the two most frequently prescribed fertility drugs are Clomiphene (better known as Clomid or Seraphene) and Pergonal, which can both coax women's systems into action.

Clomiphene – usually the first choice of the two – stimulates the pituitary gland to release the hormones that trigger ovulation. Taken in pill form, for five consecutive days – from day five of the menstrual cycle through to day nine – Clomiphene is timed so that the egg will be mature and ready to be fertilised when it's released. About 75 per cent of patients given Clomiphene will ovulate, and about 50 per cent of those will eventually conceive. In some cases, the drug works too well and leads to multiple pregnancies. About 10 per cent of women on Clomiphene will conceive twins, but fewer than 1 per cent are triplets or larger multiple pregnancies. The drug can also cause ovarian cysts.

If Clomiphene fails and tests indicate that the woman's body isn't able to produce the necessary hormones, a course of Pergonal injections may be the doctor's next decision. This is a substitute for the hormones. A battery of tests including ultrasound and daily blood tests determine exactly how the ovaries are responding to the Pergonal. About 75 per cent of Pergonal-users will ovulate; about 25 per cent of those will eventually conceive and about 20 per cent of those conceptions will be multiple pregnancies.

HOW TO TELL IF YOU'RE PREGNANT

One is constantly reading in the paper about women who are about to go to the annual Yacht Club dinner or the Rotary Club ball when, after nipping upstairs in their full-length polyester dancing outfit to have a quick widdle, they come downstairs, having given birth to a bouncing baby next to the laundry basket. I, like you, used to sneer in utter derision at these women, who had managed to experience an entire nine-month pregnancy while maintaining that they had bad flatulence or had put on a bit of weight. I no longer sneer at these people for two reasons. The first is the astonishing ability – particularly of frightened, under-age mothers – to completely ignore the symptoms of their pregnancy, hiding it both from themselves and their parents, and to continue to live under the illusion that 'it can't possibly happen to me and if I don't think about it, it will go away'.

The second reason is that with my first pregnancy I thought I had a trapped nerve in my back and didn't realise I was pregnant until I was almost five months gone. When you're pregnant you tend to spend a lot of time thinking there's something seriously wrong with you, because, contrary to what you've been told, you don't feel much like skipping around in a floaty white nightie picking daisies and spreading little beams of happiness. I spent the first three months of my pregnancy behaving like a cross between Tony Perkins in the last ten minutes of *Psycho* and Montgomery Clift after his car accident. If anyone spoke to me, I either gave them a good slapping or cried loudly till my face went puce. All this fuss depends of course on your knowing that the stork is winging his way to you clutching the baby. I wasn't aware for some months that it was the Impending Event that was making me feel so lousy – giving the lie to that other statement one hears, *You know the minute you're pregnant.*

My doctor's office looks as though war photographer Don McCullin decorated it for him in return for lancing a boil. Not for him the usual displays of comforting certificates. Next to the bed is a photo of the Wailing Wall and above the life supply of *Truss Monthly* is a large photo of a man with one leg grinning gamely and waving his crutch.

On the first visit to discover the source of my undiagnosed malaise, he suggested that I stop hoovering as I was ill from stress and excess work. I refrained from mentioning that my life was one long dress-fitting, punctuated by bouts of creative angst in Fortnum's tea rooms. But by the second visit, my beloved was making secret phonecalls to friends saying that I was in the throes of a raging nervous breakdown.

On the third visit, my doctor said my colon was twisted and by the fourth – when my chest entered the room before me – he said I was eating too much due to stress, and I had a trapped nerve in my back. Enuff is enuff, I thought, and went to stay with my friend Carol in the country, occupying myself on the train by watching my chest grow. Carol diagnosed my condition on the station platform. After asking if I'd deliberately inflated my trousers with a lilo pump, she lowered her voice to shriek, 'Bleedin' obvious, innit?' Next thing I knew, five test tubes were perched on the bath with a note saying quaintly, 'Piss in these.'

Carol's bathroom is a Kentish rendering of the golden age of the Golden Empire. If you fail to move with the agility of Sebastian Coe, you are in danger of trapping your rear end in the electronically-operated loo seat. The curtains shut if you sit on the bed and water starts running out of a gold-plated swan's head if you tread on the bath mat. So you can imagine what it was like at six in the morning trying to pee into test tubes with one foot on the onyx soap dish and one on the swan-shaped loo-roll dispenser that plays the 'Marseillaise'. The Venetian blinds were going up and down and I thought I might end up by launching the Space Shuttle.

You'll never forget the moment when you find out: this is actually true. I can remember being pulled from my prone position, crying into the shagpile with shock, by Carol's husband who was shouting somewhat bafflingly, 'This is the greatest day of my life!' I then rang the father-to-be in New York, where it was four in the morning. An almighty crash on his end of the phone heralded the sinking in of the big news and 200 roses winged their way to *chez* Chris and Carol. Being a somewhat shallow person, I must admit that the arrival of a large number of floral tributes and a fitting at the Emanuels did great things for the morale. Having got through the loathsome first few months without even knowing what was happening, even I – possibly the grumpiest girl in the western hemisphere – have to admit that it has its good points.

Pregnancy Tests

If you are very worried about being pregnant – or hoping very much that you are – you may find that this can delay your period in itself. The kits now available from chemists enable you to do your own pregnancy tests as little as a day after a missed period (even the day your period is due), provided you stick carefully to the instructions. A test should be swiftly followed by a visit to the doctor for confirmation and advice. But it is important to remember that pregnancy tests are not infallible; if the test is positive, go to your GP or Family Planning clinic at once. And if the test is negative, repeat it in a few days to make doubly certain.

Pregnancy tests work by detecting the pregnancy hormone human chorionic gondatrophin (HCG) in the urine. When an egg is in the uterus's lining, HCG prevents the next period occurring. HCG is most concentrated in the early morning, which is why all tests should be done then.

The Predictor Colour Tip This can be used the day after a missed period and you get the result in thirty minutes. If you are more than five days late you get the result in five minutes. To use: add the liquid from the dropper tube to the test tube provided; add the urine to the test tube using the dropper, remembering to practise first as it is not easy to get two drops of widdle into a test tube at seven o'clock in the morning. Put the indicator from the sealed sachet in the test tube for the appropriate time.

Discover Today This can be used the day your period is due. A positive result shows in one minute; a negative result takes three minutes. With this test you do not have to use the first of the morning's urine. To use: with the dropper provided, add the urine sample to the test tube containing a powder; add the key to the test tube to read the result.

Clear Blue This can be used the day your period is due; the result shows in thirty minutes. This test requires the first morning's urine. To use: hold the sampler in the stream of urine (which means you probably wee all over your hand); place in the first well on the test stand. Leave for ten minutes. Then rinse and place in the second well for ten minutes. Then rinse and place in the third well for the final ten minutes. I have to say that I tried this test once while on holiday in

Australia and was unable to tell whether my ball had turned blue because the test uses a small ball trapped in the end of a plastic wand, which I found very symbolic. I then had to ring my best friend long-distance from Sydney to ask if it *sounded* like it was blue to her...

Boots Home Pregnancy Test This can be used when your period is one day late; the result takes thirty minutes. If three to five days late, you get the result in fifteen minutes, and if you are more than six days late, five minutes. This test requires the first morning's urine. To use: add the liquid from the dropper tube to the test tube. Add the urine to the test tube. Place the indicator in the test tube and wait for the appropriate length of time. Rinse and read the results.

The Clear Blue One-Step (which sounds like something they do in the North-east on *Come Dancing*). This can be used on the day your period should have started. It does require the first morning's urine and the result appears within three minutes. To use: once again, hold the absorbent sampler in a stream of urine. Replace the cap (bit late!). A blue line appears in the small window to show the test is complete. A blue line in the large window indicates positive results.

First Response This test can be used on the day your period is due. The result appears in five minutes and does not require the first morning's urine. To use: with the dropper provided, add the urine to the test tube and leave for five minutes. Then, add to the well on the test stand and allow the well to drain. A pink colour in the well indicates a positive result.

Pregnancy Symptoms

A missed period When the egg is fertilised, the body immediately prepares a place for it by enriching the womb lining, which provides nourishment and protection. However, some women still have a period after a pregnancy has begun, though the bleeding is usually of shorter duration than usual. As the pregnancy grows, it fills the womb and the lining provides a base for the placenta. From this time on, no blood should be lost at all and you will get no further periods until several weeks after the pregnancy is over.

Morning sickness Hormone levels alter dramatically when you are first pregnant. The mother may find it hard to adjust to the massive doses of oestrogen and progesterone which are in her system. Then she feels sick. This can seem worse in the morning. To combat nausea, don't stop eating, but try to avoid the obvious things like very fatty or spicy foods. Eat little and often. Sit up slowly when you wake up and take things easy. If you are not managing to keep things down, see your doctor immediately. Or try alternative remedies like herbal tea, ginger, Brewer's Yeast, acupressure or aromatherapy.

You may have sore breasts You may also notice that they are getting steadily larger.

Expanding waistline Even early on, you may find that your body lays down extra fat to prepare itself for pregnancy. Or your bigger tummy may simply be due to gas distension.

Tiredness Extreme tiredness often takes many newly pregnant women by surprise. You may wish to sleep all day but this tiredness will pass.

Needing to wee frequently This is because of your womb, which puts pressure on your bladder.

LOSING A BABY

Miscarriage is surprisingly common – as many as 100,000 women in this country are likely to miscarry this year. Miscarriage means the loss of a baby at any time before twenty-eight weeks of pregnancy, but only about 3 per cent of miscarriages take place after the fourteenth week. It's also possible to miscarry even before you know you're pregnant, as this often happens at a time when you would have had your period. It may be impossible to tell the difference between a very heavy period and an early miscarriage. Doctors estimate that one in three pregnancies end this way.

Types of Miscarriage

Threatened miscarriage Most miscarriages start with bleeding and pain. Many pregnant women – perhaps half – have some bleeding, and less than half of these will go on to miscarry. No damage is done to a baby by a threatened miscarriage. If you start to bleed in pregnancy, you should ring your doctor. He will probably advise you to avoid sex for the near future and also tell you to go to bed immediately, but it still isn't clear if bed-rest helps. He may arrange a scan to make sure all is well with the baby.

Inevitable miscarriage If you are going to miscarry, there will come a point of no return. You may start to shiver or feel sick, or you may feel pain and experience heavy, bright vaginal bleeding as your uterus contracts. If you are showing signs of miscarrying, your doctor will try and find out what is happening, depending on how far your pregnancy has advanced and whether or not you're in hospital. You may be frightened by what you see during a miscarriage: in early pregnancy, the miscarriage will seem like a heavy period, with a lot of blood and some clots, but if it is a late miscarriage some women actually see their babies. Strange as this may sound, this seems to be something they never regret – seeing the baby confirms that it was real, and gives them something to grieve about which is a very important part of the recovery process.

Nowadays, miscarriage seems something of a taboo. While other subjects are discussed quite openly, a woman's miscarriage can remain quite secret and therefore difficult to grieve over.

Incomplete miscarriage Sometimes fragments of tissue are left behind in the womb and there is a danger that, if they are left there, they can cause heavy bleeding and an infection. If there is any sign that this has happened, the doctor will probably give you a D & C (Dilation and Curettage) under a light anaesthetic, which means the cervix is stretched and any remaining tissue is scraped from the lining of the womb. If doctors think that you might have a tubal pregnancy, you may have a laparoscopy (where a micro-sized tube is inserted into the womb through a tiny incision in your belly button) to investigate.

What Causes Miscarriage?

Foetal abnormality The most likely cause of an early miscarriage. Between 50–60 per cent of miscarriages before twelve weeks have defects in their chromosomes. Many of these mistakes are completely random and do not effect your future pregnancies.

Environmental hazards Visual Display Units may be another potential hazard. Although they give off a very low level of radiation, higher incidences of miscarriages, stillbirths and birth defects have been found among women who use VDUs. It's very important for all VDU users to have a protective screen fitted over their VDU which filters out many of the potentially harmful rays. Environmental pollutants, such as chemicals in drinking water, lead in petrol, pesticides on fruit and vegetables, may also be to blame – so pregnant women should buy a water filter or drink bottled water, and stick to organic fruits and vegetables, increasingly available in supermarkets. They do cost a bit more but your health – and your baby's – make it worthwhile.

Cervical incompetence Some late miscarriages may happen when the neck of the womb is unable to hold the baby in place and opens up too early. A small stitch can be placed in the cervix to prevent this happening in future pregnancies.

Faults in the immune system In some women, the immune system seems to attack the baby and reject her as if she was a foreign body. Tests and treatment can now do a great deal to prevent this happening. Immunology is the newest treatment on offer for miscarriage; it is directed at the woman's immune system – the mechanism that protects her against harmful substances or illnesses. Some women lack the antibodies necessary to support their pregnancies. The treatment offered to them consists of injections of white blood cells from the woman's partner. It is not available everywhere and is also not suitable for every woman who miscarries.

Starting again It is a good idea to talk to someone who has shared your own anxieties. The Miscarriage Association (address below) can help you to find someone, but don't be afraid to bombard your doctor with questions. Write down his replies if you're worried you'll forget. He'll probably advise you to wait three months after an early pregnancy, and for late miscarriages the advice is normally to wait a month for each month that you carried your baby. You should try to relax as much as possible – perhaps have a holiday – and avoid all the health hazards you possibly can.

Finally, think positively. Women are very fertile after a miscarriage and even after four or more miscarriages you still have a 40 per cent chance of having a healthy baby next time.

The Miscarriage Association, 18 Stoneybrook Close, West Bretton, Wakefield, West Yorkshire WF4 4TP (0924 85515).

Chapter Two

Thinking

Beautiful

Thoughts

During the last month of both my pregnancies I began to take on an almost uncanny resemblance to Guy the Gorilla, after he'd been stuffed. I gazed down in the bath at what must have been the largest stomach in Britain not involved in professional darts. My little fat legs stuck out from underneath. At least, I think they did, but I hadn't actually seen them for some time.

Baths had become such a depressing experience that I contemplated joining one of those mysterious religious sects that insist you wash yourself under a large tarpaulin. Invariably, I would wonder what on earth my stomach was going to look like afterwards – worse still, what my bosom was going to look like, having grown from a size 30 trainer bra to a 44D cup. With my mind boggling from these thoughts, I would haul myself out of the bath and experience further torture over the weighing machine. Everyone I knew was waiting to see if I'd managed to put on a 'Kylie Minogue', as it was widely believed I must be about to give birth to a fully-grown Australian singer.

I have to tell you that once you've put on four and a half stone, as I did, it becomes almost impossible to look like Camille as you recline on the sofa, recovering from the last triple-decker sandwich. One afternoon I was concentrating on looking beautifully Rubensesque, and my husband lay next to me, gazing in a rather awestruck fashion, I thought. After a lengthy pause, he leaned over and whispered in my ear, 'Darling, did you know that since you've been pregnant you've grown a sweet little moustache?'

Something I found even more annoying was the sense of having to share my body with somebody else – the constant kicking and thudding, the fact that Peaches was trapped beneath my ribs for about three months – during which time I resorted to standing on my head to alleviate the pressure. In the middle of the night, she would do disco-dancing inferno and I could tell when she fell asleep early each morning, only to be amazed at how she could sleep soundly through all the housework.

Other women feel that they aren't just sharing their body with somebody small and potentially extremely cute, they are sharing it with every Tom, Dick and Harriet they meet. Somehow, a big stomach acts as a magnet: even people you don't know very well long to touch it. Instead of the series of wolf whistles you might have become accustomed to from workmen hanging off scaffoldings, you get all these questions about when it's due and what sex it is, as they peer intently at your stomach.

Having a huge stomach is like buying a dog. Suddenly everyone else in the street has one and people act like you're in an exclusive club. Other pregnant women start chatting to you in the park; women with pushchairs smile a small, secret grin at you. Everyone ceases to look at your face (which is probably just as well).

It's very tempting simply to collapse on the couch clutching a large box of Mr Kipling cakes, while the workout video flickers silently on the telly, just to stop you feeling guilty. I was haunted by dreams in which I was going to be pregnant for ever, meaning I'd always have to go to the loo every fifteen minutes, and be forced to wear nothing but those red floral dresses that Sheila Kitzinger's so fond of. But it doesn't last for ever, you survive it all – and there's that little bit of heaven at the end of it . . .

ANTENATAL CARE

At your first antenatal visit (following your GP's confirmation of your pregnancy) a form will be filled out giving details of your medical and obstetric history, and it will obviously help if you can remember the date of your last period. The date of the baby's birth is calculated as 280 days from the first day of this period. Antenatal visits will take place on a monthly basis until the twenty-fourth week of pregnancy. For the next eight weeks they will be fortnightly, after which they will be weekly.

Antenatal Tests

At each visit you'll be weighed, have your blood pressure taken and your urine tested; your abdomen will be examined and the baby's heart beat listened to. At the beginning and end of the pregnancy you may receive a vaginal examination and a blood test. Sometimes at the first visit, but more usually at around eighteen weeks, there'll be an ultrasound examination. If you or your baby is considered to be at risk, you may have an amniocentesis test.

Urine testing Urine is tested for protein and sugar. This is the doctor's way of making sure that you are not developing either toxaemia or diabetes, both of which are commonly triggered in pregnancy. Also, infections in the urine are more common when a woman is expecting a baby.

Your blood tests A number of things will be discovered from this small sample. Your blood group is very important, just in case a transfusion might ever be needed. There are four blood groups: A, B, AB and O. The other important aspect of the blood group is whether you are rhesus positive or rhesus negative. Being rhesus negative can cause many serious complications during pregnancy if left untreated. Antibodies formed in subsequent pregnancies in rhesus negative women can harm a rhesus positive baby. This is nowadays prevented by a suitable injection after delivery of a first baby.

Your haemoglobin will also be tested from your blood sample. The haemoglobin in your blood cells determines its ability to transport oxygen around the body. Haemoglobin can fall and then you get anaemia. The normal level of haemoglobin is around 90–100 per cent, but because of the water in your body during pregnancy, 80 per cent is normal. You will also receive a test for Rubella, to make sure you are immune, and, if you are not, you'll be vaccinated just after the baby is born. The hospital will test for evidence of spina bifida; if the baby has a deformed spine, an abnormal substance called alpha-foeto protein appears in the blood. Women of African or Asian origin will also be tested for the sickle cell trait. If the test is positive, your partner will be tested, too. The same is true for Tay-Sachs' disease. Your blood will be tested for evidence of syphilis. Aids tests are offered to those who think they are at risk, but are never done without consent.

Ultrasound examination Ultrasound was first used to detect submarines by warships during World War One. In antenatal care it is used to find out how the baby is growing, whether there are twins, and also, if the woman has had previous miscarriages, to make sure everything is going OK. Ultrasounds also show us if there is a breech presentation (which means the baby is upside down). Breech presentation is the commonest malpresentation seen during the ante-natal period. Babies are often breech up to about thirty-four weeks, but at this time they usually kick themselves round the right way. If they do not do this by that point, it is usually because the legs – instead of being flexed – have become extended. If breech presentation is discovered early, the doctor may try to turn your baby around. If this is successful, it prevents a breech delivery, but a doctor will not attempt to turn a baby after thirty-six weeks. In any case, by then the baby is much too big, and so you and your doctor will have to discuss the best way to deliver it.

Ultrasound also shows up the position of the placenta, and can detect some foetal abnormalities.

Amniocentesis Your doctor may decide that you need a specialised test. This is the most common of these: a procedure which entails a needle being inserted through the abdominal wall into the amniotic sac in the uterus. Fluid can then be withdrawn and examined. Before the needle is inserted, an ultrasound is done to make sure that the baby and the placenta will not be damaged. It is usually done at about fourteen to sixteen weeks to detect Down's syndrome and spina bifida babies. The test can also determine the sex of the baby. Diagnosis is made by taking some of the baby's skin cells, contained in the amniotic fluid, and growing them in a culture medium. The laboratory work takes between two and four weeks to be completed, and the test may have to be repeated.

The risk of having a mongol baby is about 1 in 1,000 in women up to the age of thirty-five, but after this age the risk is greater. By the time a woman is forty, the risk is 1 in 80. It's now recommended that all women over the age of thirty-five should have this test, even though the procedure itself does carry a slight risk of miscarriage (1 per cent). Doctors recommend that, if you are going to have amniocentesis, you should have carefully considered whether or not you would then have a termination if the test proved positive. Otherwise you will be under pressure to make a decision very rapidly, and in a very emotional state of mind.

Amniocentesis to detect spina bifida is only done when the blood test has been positive, there is a family history of spina bifida, or where the woman has already had a spina bifida baby.

Common Ailments

It is important at all of your antenatal visits to write down anything that is worrying you, so that you don't forget to ask, and also to try to build up a feeling of ease around doctors and midwives, which will hold you in good stead during your labour. Many antenatal clinics seem crowded and rather frantic, and you may worry about holding others up. But don't. Your primary responsibility is to yourself and your own peace of mind, and pregnant women do tend to suffer from vivid imaginations which plague them with doubts and worries in the middle of the night, and many of these can be settled during your clinic visit.

Anaemia During pregnancy a woman's body may not be able to supply the extra demand for iron and folic acid. The drain on your resources can make you anaemic and the answer is to take extra iron and folic acid as prescribed by your doctor. Anaemia is usually detected through a blood test, but you may also be aware of symptoms like feeling excessively tired.

Vaginal discharge All vaginal secretions increase during pregnancy. However, if this is causing itching or soreness, you should consult your doctor, as it could be thrush. Thrush is a yeast-like germ which likes to live in warmth, moisture and sugar, all of which are present in a pregnant woman's vaginal and vulval area. The discharge is usually white or yellow and curd-like, and this germ can be passed on by your husband, who may also be feeling a slight skin irritation. Thrush may start with itching but often becomes very painful. It is usually effectively treated with nystatin, although, as with any complaint during pregnancy, do consider some of the natural, alternative treatments before you opt for drugs like this. You can find books on homeopathic and alternative remedies for women at your local health food store or in your public library.

Alternatively, you may be suffering from a trichomonal infection, which again causes a discharge and irritation. This is passed on by an infected man, who will probably not know he has it. The usual treatment is a course of Flagyl, and the male partner must be treated at the same time. You musn't drink alcohol during treatment.

Gonorrhoea is a common VD which can recur in pregnant as well as non-pregnant women. It is often symptomless, but the disease may give rise to a vaginal discharge with pain when you pee. Any pregnant woman who thinks she may have had intercourse with someone infected with gonorrhoea must seek help. This infection can be cleared up by an injection or a course of injections, but it can infect the baby's eyes if it is still present at delivery.

The same applies if you suffer from herpes. Your doctor must always be consulted to make sure that any herpes infection is cleared away before the baby is due to be delivered, to prevent infection of the baby. Many doctors prefer, if you have an active herpes lesion, to deliver the baby by caesarean.

A blood-stained discharge can indicate a threatened miscarriage in the early weeks, or, if it happens in late pregnancy, it could signal the onset of your labour. If it happens in the middle, it is sometimes the result of cervical erosion, which does no harm and will often mend itself after the pregnancy is over. Obviously, a doctor must be consulted if you see any signs of blood because on rare occasions this can be a sign of something more serious.

A watery discharge at the end of your pregnancy is usually a signal that the baby is on her way. It can either be a whoosh of water or a drip of water, but either way it means that the membranes surrounding the baby have broken, also known as your waters breaking.

Varicose veins A pregnant woman has four pints more blood than normal and because of this her veins may become dilated. In some women, especially those with a family history of varicose veins, veins can become so dilated that they become varicose. Avoid tight socks or stockings, and sit down whenever you can. Small varicose veins usually disappear once the baby is born. Some women suffer from varicose veins on the vulva, particularly after repeated pregnancies. These do not cause any difficulties during the delivery, and, while they are uncomfortable, they do disappear without treatment after the baby is born.

Piles are varicose veins up your bum. These are very painful and usually occur during the later weeks (and they can itch like crazy, too) when the baby is pressing down heavily. Constipation and standing up too much both aggravate this condition. They can be eased by rest, a fibre-rich diet, and soothing ointments. Do not be embarrassed to mention this problem at your antenatal clinic.

Heartburn Heartburn can be relieved by chewing a small, alkaline indigestion tablet, but indigestion is best avoided by having small amounts of food often, and steering clear of anything very greasy and spicy.

Leg cramps, numbness and tingling All of these are normal in mid-pregnancy. Leg cramp is triggered by suddenly stretching your legs, and the cause is unknown. It is not a sign of a lack of calcium or salt, and is best cured by getting your partner to rub your leg ferociously. Numbness and tingling in the hands is caused by fluid retention pressing on nerves. No treatment is required, other than in severe instances, where a small pain relief tablet may help.

Pregnancy Complications

Your antenatal clinic is also the place to discuss any more serious worries you may have. It is very important to remember your regular appointments, so that, should anything be wrong, it can be diagnosed as early as possible.

Toxaemia This usually happens late in pregnancy, after thirty-six weeks, but can occur any time after twenty weeks, and you may hear your doctor calling it pre-eclampsia, or pre-eclamptic toxaemia. Pre-eclampsia includes hypertension, which is raised blood pressure, protein in your urine, and swelling of the legs, hands, feet or even face. The normal blood pressure of a healthy pregnant woman is about 110/80, but you will be regarded as having hypertension if yours has risen to 140/90. No one knows the causes of toxaemia, but your doctor will attempt to control these different symptoms until the baby is big enough to be delivered. If your case is mild, you will be allowed to rest at home, but severe cases usually mean being taken into hospital. This is because a mild case can escalate suddenly. Women with toxaemia often feel perfectly well, but it is important never to risk this condition progressing. Severe pre-eclamptic toxaemia sometimes requires sedatives and anti-hypertension drugs. As soon as the woman's blood pressure has fallen, steps are taken to deliver the baby.

Eclampsia is a form of toxaemia that has been untreated. In addition to the swelling, blood pressure problems and urine abnormalities, the patient also develops headaches and fits. This is dangerous to both mother and baby.

Placenta praevia The placenta is normally positioned in the upper part of your uterus, but it can sometimes get positioned in the lower area and block the birth outlet. In this case there is a risk of severe bleeding as the uterus stretches in preparation for labour and the placenta starts to separate.

Placenta praevia can be detected by a scan, and if the case is severe, the baby will be delivered by caesarean. In a mild case, labour will be allowed to continue normally, but the membranes may be artificially broken.

The cause is not known – it is very rare with a first baby, and occurs in around one in a hundred pregnancies.

WHAT KIND OF BIRTH DO YOU WANT?

You are legally entitled to have your baby absolutely anywhere you choose, providing that your doctor is in agreement and the hospital you have chosen has a bed for you. But many women end up going to just any hospital, without thought as to what would be the most appropriate choice of birth. The alternatives available may not even have been discussed beforehand – you could find yourself booked into the nearest maternity hospital, only to find it isn't really suitable.

It's important right from the start of your pregnancy to ask as many questions as you feel you need to. Every birth is unique, and you want to ensure that yours is absolutely unforgettable, and indisputably the happiest day of your life. For a lot of women it isn't – and this is in large part due to the fact that their choices and rights and feelings have been ignored. This can be avoided by knowing exactly what you want, going to a place where you're most likely to get it, and by refusing to be bullied by doctors – who like to believe that what they say is gospel even though it contradicts your gut instincts.

Where to Have Your Baby

Hospital Large teaching hospitals often specialise in delivering babies. You will probably already have been visiting your local hospital's antenatal clinic. A hospital birth is good for those who enjoy the feeling of security provided by having lots of doctors around and plenty of medical equipment – which of course is excellent if any medical complications occur. Many hospitals give relaxation, mothercraft, and preparation-for-birth classes, which start around week twenty-seven of pregnancy and can be very helpful.

Hospital policies vary, as do the doctors working in them. Some are against inducing labour and may even allow you to go up to three weeks past your due date (heaven forbid!). Others may induce you after only a few days. Some perform more caesareans than others, so it's important to find out as much as you can beforehand. Often there are open evenings for people to raise their queries.

The disadvantages are the large busy wards, the lack of privacy and romance (which you may have dreamed of) – the general air of impersonality. There are frequently long waits at antenatal clinics, and very often a lack of continuity of care. You may see as many as five doctors during your pregnancy, which doesn't make for bonding with your obstetrician.

The Cottage Hospital Sadly, many of these small and older hospitals which cater solely for childbirth have now been phased out. But some areas do still have these little gems and they are perfect for women who like a more relaxed and informal atmosphere, as they are much cosier and more comfortable than most teaching hospitals. At the birth, the monitoring may be done either electronically or by hand using an ear trumpet! Pain relief will be more limited; unfortunately, some of these small hospitals still don't give epidurals. The main disadvantage is that these hospitals are not always able to cope with serious complications. If these do occur, you might find yourself being rushed to another hospital in an ambulance.

Home With a home birth, you have your delivery, your post- and antenatal care all in your own, cosy home. These are becoming more popular again after many years of being virtually unheard of – but they are still more common among mothers who have already had a first baby with no complications. Many doctors are still against the idea and it is easier to have a home birth with a doctor's support. You can start to arrange one by writing to your local director of midwifery – it is then up to the authorities to provide your medical care. You may find that your midwife has sole responsibility for antenatal care and labour, but in some districts there are rules which mean that a doctor must do the stitching.

You can deliver where you like, and be surrounded by your family, who may be able to assist you in natural methods of pain relief such as breathing exercises and massage, unless they're my family in which case they'll be singing and eating and completely ignoring you. Mums who've had a home birth give glowing reports of how relaxed and in control of the situation they felt. You have a continuity of care which inspires confidence. All the decisions are yours; there's no journey to the hospital and back and your baby will spend the first days of her life in peace and quiet.

Bear in mind that you may have a big initial battle to get a home birth, and that you must be prepared to risk a complication-free labour.

The Domino Scheme I heard about the Domino Scheme from my health visitor who was very involved in the new system. Domino is short for Dom-in-and-out. Although you have your baby in the hospital, she is delivered by the local midwife, from whom you've also received your antenatal care, and you leave hospital six hours after the birth. This is a good idea for anyone who is hoping for a short stay in hospital and has good back-up at home. Having said this, I can't imagine there are many mothers who would feel that keen on leaping out of bed and going home after six hours. And staying in hospital after the birth is basically the last good rest – and good fuss – that you're going to get for some time to come.

Like home birth, the advantage of this scheme is that you have a marvellous continuity of care from your midwife, who will know your exact thoughts and wishes on the birth. There is also a short absence from the rest of the family who will be able to share the first few days of the baby's life and not feel left out at all.

Private hospitals Having a baby privately has many advantages – although at a price, which often runs quite high if you choose to stay in hospital for a week. Although most hospitals provide a private service, only a little over 1 per cent of women in Britain actually use it. If you are hoping to have an 'alternative' birth, private services are much more amenable to these ideas.

If you are paying for your antenatal care, too, which most people do if they are having a private birth, you will see the same consultant throughout your pregnancy and build up an unshakeable bond. At times you may wish you were married to him, rather than your husband.

If there are any complications during the birth, private medical insurance covers all of them, but otherwise you will have to pay for the delivery, anaesthetists and your room – which can cost anything from £100 a night to £600 a night, depending on where you are. The Portland, where Fergie had Princess Beatrice, is at the top end of the price scale (£600 for the first twenty-four hours). St Mary's, Paddington, where Princess Diana had her children and I had mine, is about £120 a night and just as nice as the Savoy, if you ask me. (And could I now have my next birth free?)

47

Alternative Birth

Water birth Mention alternative birth to many National Health doctors and they get a glazed expression on their faces like Victorian ladies who've taken strychnine. This is because they have an instant mental picture of you using a birthing chair as a sort of pommel, with the baby half-way out of you and not a machine in sight. Or else they imagine you and your partner are hoping to involve them in a water birth, in which case they're probably wondering if their rather dashing day-glo shorts bought on a cycling holiday in the Dordogne will do for the event or whether they should get hold of something more dapper.

Actually, I've never been that keen on water births for three reasons. The first is that I'm obsessively tidy, and because it would be likely to take place at home, I can just see the water sloshing over the edge of the tank sending me into a frenzy of mopping-up mid-labour. Secondly, there's always the danger of the boiler conking out and you being left panting in three feet of rapidly freezing water. I always did wonder how women who have inordinately long labours stop their hands and feet from turning into Dead Sea sponges. Thirdly, there's the prospect of seeing one's doctor literally stripped bare, and, knowing my luck, probably wearing a pair of Homme bikini-thong briefs in maroon Paisley.

A number of my friends have had water births at the same private hospital in London, and one of them mentioned to me the other day that if she'd wanted they would have been willing to procure a dolphin to assist in the birth. I didn't really get any more details out of her about Flipper's exact involvement in the proceedings because she said in the end she just opted for the New Age cassette of Carl Sagan reading poems to a backdrop of crashing waves and rather raucous seagulls.

Leboyer Water births are of course related in many ways to this method of childbirth. Leboyer wisely believed that a baby would be calmer and happier if she was born into calm, happy surroundings where lights were dimmed and noise kept to the minimum except for maybe a little soft music tinkling away. A Leboyer baby is delivered on to the mother's stomach, as both of mine were, and then the cord is allowed to stop throbbing naturally before the doctor cuts it. Then the baby is given a tepid bath, which is meant to remind her of the womb. Most hospitals practise some of this, but you will have to make absolutely sure if you plan to have a completely Leboyer-style baby that it is writ large on your notes!

Active birth This approach was perfected at Michel Odent's clinic in Pithiviers in France. Women following this natural childbirth practice are encouraged to follow their instincts throughout the labour. At the hospital, Odent created what was known as a 'primitive' room, which further encouraged women not to just lie back and give birth but to move around and stand up. The room had things like mattresses on the floor, and even bean bags. He also discovered that many women enjoyed a luke-warm bath while in labour – and some even preferred to stay put and give birth in the water.

It has been found that staying mobile does seem to make contractions stronger – and so these births are faster. Being upright has the added bonus of utilising gravity – and, because kneeling and squatting increases the size of the pelvic area, there is less of a need for either caesareans or episiotomies. A few NHS hospitals have been influenced by the active birth idea, and have introduced birthing chairs and beds which can be adjusted to suit the woman's chosen position.

Your Birth Plan

Many times while writing this book I have been aware that a woman paying for her birth is likely to have a very different time from someone using NHS facilities, where there is undoubtedly less choice and flexibility. Sadly, many busy hospitals are just not willing to go along with birth plans from women who long for dim lights, soft music, or even a degree of privacy away from marauding herds of student doctors peering up their nether regions every twenty minutes. Nevertheless, it is imperative to write a birth plan. Go through it carefully with the midwife and make sure it's attached to your notes in hospital. Obviously, no birth plan should be so rigid that if anything were to go wrong you'd still expect your doctor to be struggling with the ghetto blaster to get Luther Vandross on at exactly the right pitch, but a realistic birth plan can make all the difference. Labour is not the time to start trying out everything you learnt on the office assertiveness course – you won't feel like arguing over pain killers between contractions. And don't forget to make sure your husband knows exactly what you're aiming at, too. You might like to consider the following points in drawing up your plan.

1. During labour and the birth will I be able to have someone with me?
2. Can I have an active birth and move around if I want or will I have to lie on my back the whole time? (This is often just to be convenient for the doctors and can lengthen the second stage of your labour considerably.)
3. How many episiotomies and caesareans does the hospital perform in a month?
4. Will the baby be constantly attached to various monitors?
5. What is the arrival procedure – do they still shave mothers?
6. In the event of a caesarean will I be able to have my partner or a friend present?
7. Do they try to set time limits on labour during the various stages rather than letting mothers follow their own instincts?
8. Will they induce labour?
9. If I need an epidural in the dead of night, will there DEFINITELY be someone there to give it to me?
10. Will the hospital let my baby stay with me all the time, day and night, preferably in bed with me? If not, will they let me check out immediately if everything has gone well?
11. Do hospital staff encourage mothers to breast-feed?
12. Do they approve of feeding on demand?
13. Is there a special care baby unit at the hospital?
14. Will visitors be allowed?
15. How much privacy will I get?
16. How many members of staff are likely to help at the birth? How many doctors will change shifts during the labour?

The National Perinatal Epidemiology Unit, Radcliffe Infirmary, Oxford, have published a factual guide, *Where to Be Born*, available from them for £2.00.

The National Childbirth Trust gives local information, plus practical advice before and after birth. Local lists from NCT, Alexandra House, Oldham Terrace, London W3 6NH (081 992 8637). Enclose SAE. They also publish a leaflet, *Giving Birth at Home* (£1 plus 25p p & p).

The Independent Midwives Association, 35 Cleveland Road, London SW13 (071 278 6783).

Active Birth Movement, 55 Dartmouth Park Road, London NW5 1SL (071 267 3006). Facilities include water birth pools for hire: approximately £125 for four weeks.

Society to Support Home Confinements, Ludgate, Ludgate Lane, Wolsingham, Bishop Auckland, Co. Durham DL13 3HA (0388 528044).

LOOK GOOD AND FEEL GOOD

Each time I have been pregnant my husband has always made a great deal of fuss about whether I was thinking beautiful thoughts. In studies it has been proved that the state of the mother's mind and emotions has a great effect upon her unborn baby.

This may seem like a pressure – not only are you pregnant and fat and knackered, but suddenly you are expected to change from being a face-stuffing-drink-swilling-fag-ashing-lazy-loafing-cellulite-covered lump, lying in bed wearing nothing but a four-week-old corn plaster, into a sunny-natured fresh-smelling cross between Anne of Green Gables and the Virgin Mary.

As soon as you are pregnant, if you haven't already been in training for the event, you'll find there are lots of things you will have to give up. Suddenly the doctor informs you that being fat isn't just a phase you've been going through since you were twelve, and that he knows all about the family pack of fun-sized Marathons you consumed the night before. I found the whole danger of putting on too much weight during my pregnancy impossible to believe in. Unfortunately, I'm one of those people who can eat CONTINUOUSLY without a) being sick, b) experiencing guilt, or c) having visions of myself in six months' time resembling a waterlogged sea slug wearing a viyella nightie, with feet in stirrups.

Some people will suggest that you pin photographs of glamorous women on to the fridge door, like Raquel Welch aged about seventy still looking ten years younger than Bonnie Langford and claiming it's all because she didn't eat Twix when she was pregnant. Personally speaking, as someone who is rather portly during pregnancy, I would recommend putting pictures of Dame Flora Robson and Red Rum on to the Electrolux, thus giving yourself a boost each time you look at them.

You'll have given up smoking, having first psyched yourself up, repeating, mantra-like, that you truly are sick of smelling like Batley Variety Club at 3 am, you're sick of having jaundice at the end of two fingers and teeth that look like the dog on the Rabies posters. Try not to regard every major domestic crisis as solved by the comforting touch of Swan Vesta on cigarette, instead enjoy the new conversations you'll be having with friends: 'It's just like having an amputation, really – my finger actually itches where the cigarette used to be.' Added to which, giving up smoking gives you another excuse to eat sweets . . .

Finally, in the top three of becoming a beautiful person, is of course the demon drink. Usually giving up drinking is brought about by feelings of abject remorse and humiliation as you remember the office party. Shudders can be evoked weeks later as you recall French kissing on the fire escape with the janitor, finishing up with a tour de force performance, carried out entirely knickerless and without a safety net, of 'Gimme the Moonlight' from the top of a tin filing cabinet in Accounts. When you're pregnant, drink must be banished from your life, even though you probably think that parties won't seem the same now that all you'll consume is a pickled herring and a glass of Tizer.

Eating Enough for Forty-Seven

During your pregnancy you may find it almost impossible to eat small amounts. I think it's all very well giving great advice about keeping your weight down and eating healthily, but often the reality is that you're waking up in the middle of the night fantasising about jam roly-poly with Marmite on it. However, the usual medical advice is not to put on more than 28lb (12kg), which is considered sufficient to support and build up a 7lb 7oz (3.4kg) baby. And there are certain foods that are crucial to pregnancy and contain essential nutritional elements. So make sure you eat them in between the fondant delicacies you smuggled out of the corner shop under cover of darkness.

Don't fight cravings, but try to satisfy them in healthy ways. If what you long for is extremely bad for you, try to think of a substitute – for example, dried fruit instead of chocolate bars or unbuttered popcorn instead of crisps. Nausea usually fades after the third month, but food aversions and cravings continue throughout pregnancy. I thought that my craving for a pea soup was fairly revolting until I met a woman at my doctor's who told me she was just embarking on eating her second hotwater bottle. She earnestly explained that she liked the wobbly bit the lid fitted into best . . .

It is important not to give into the temptation to diet right at the

end of pregnancy to give yourself a head start after the baby's born. This is dangerous; it is both very bad for the baby and for your performance during labour.

Protein Pork, poultry, liver, LOBSTER (!), sardines, kippers, sole, salmon, lamb, pilchards, oysters, eggs, cheese, milk, peas, nuts, beans, lentils, beef, haddock.

Carbohydrate Cakes, bread, pasta, potatoes, cereals.

Fats Butter, mayonnaise, lard, cooking oils, nut and fish oils.

Vitamins Vitamin A, B1, B2, C, D, E, are all needed, but remember that if you are eating properly each day you definitely won't need vitamin pills, and as it is possible to overdose on some of them, I would steer away unless medically advised to take a supplement.

Iron This is used to make haemoglobin, which then makes up part of the red blood cells which carry the oxygen around your body. A lack of iron causes you to become anaemic. Almost all meat has iron in it, especially liver. So do broccoli, spinach, cabbage, sprouts, and eggs. So you see, it really is important to eat your greens. Your doctor may recommend an iron supplement.

Calcium This helps the baby's bones to grow! Sometimes, if a mother-to-be is really short of calcium, the baby's drain on her resources will weaken her own bones. Calcium is in your daily cheese, milk, and also the cream you may be lavishly pouring over that jam roly-poly and Marmite. It is also in fish and nuts.

Things you only need a tiny bit of Iodine, copper, phosphorus, manganese, magnesium, iodine and cobalt. These do many different jobs in your body including helping to form tissue and blood, so a complete absence of them is damaging. But again, as long as you are eating plenty of the above foods, you should be getting sufficient trace elements.

Folic acid This is in leaf vegetables, livers and kidneys, and yeasty foods. Some doctors will recommend that you take folic acid tablets to supplement your intake during the pregnancy.

Are you too tired to cook? Here are some suggestions for things that are nutritious, packed with protein, and very easy to fix: egg, chicken salad or tuna sandwiches – adding a tomato gives extra vitamin C; celery sticks spread with cheeses or peanut butter and raisins; a slice of wholegrain bread with sliced tomato and cheese put under the grill; a fruit plate with cottage cheese and wholegrain crackers; milkshakes made with fruit and dairy ice-cream.

These may not assuage your partner's need for chops and two veg, so why not use this excuse to inveigle him into going out and getting a takeaway? Or even learning to cook . . .

Dangerous foods An infection found in soft cheese, pâtés and chilled foods, listeria can kill an unborn baby – or, if she survives, leave her brain-damaged. These foods are to be avoided at all costs during pregnancy. Until December 1988, most people had never heard of listeria, and were horrified when it was identified as being the cause of many miscarriages and stillbirths. Pregnant women are particularly at risk because their immune system switches off during pregnancy in order to let the baby grow. Many women don't even realise they have listeria until it is too late, because of its mild, flu-like symptoms.

Salmonella poisoning is another danger, and you should be scrupulous with food hygiene to prevent bacteria of any kind reaching you or your unborn baby.

Between the listeria and the egg and beef scares, you'll be wondering if *anything* is safe to eat. Stay healthy (and calm!) by following these tips:

1. Never buy food that is past the sell-by date, and remember to shop in busy stores where there is a rapid turnover of stock.
2. Poultry should look firm and shiny and should be eaten within three days of buying it. It must also be thoroughly defrosted.
3. All fresh fish should have firm flesh and a clean smell. If it looks revoltingly watery or greenish or blueish, do not buy it. Fish should be eaten the same day as purchase.
4. Fresh fruit and vegetables are safe, but must be washed very thoroughly before eating, especially if you are going to eat them raw. If you are abroad, peel all of your fruit and do not eat salads.
5. Do not use the same knife or surfaces for raw meat as for cooked foods and salads, and do not allow the liquids from frozen products to come into contact with any other food or surfaces.
6. Never put hot or warm food into the fridge, as this heats up the food next to it so that the bacteria in it can grow. Always wrap up any raw meat before putting it in the fridge.

7. Do not let anyone with diarrhoea or flu-like symptoms prepare your food.
8. When reheating food, make sure it reaches boiling temperature all the way through.
9. Eat food within one hour of cooking. If you are eating out or on holiday, make sure you avoid places where the food is just warm and may have been standing around in the kitchen all afternoon.
10. Keep the fridge at the right temperature. Freezers should be below −18 degrees Centigrade and fridges should be between 2–8 degrees Centigrade. You can buy a small fridge thermometer in most hardware stores.
11. As well as soft cheese, pâtés and chilled food, avoid pre-packed salads, and highly processed foods like hamburgers, sausages and salami.

Exercise Those Aches Away

For the initial months of my second pregnancy, the only real exercise I indulged in, apart from looking after my daughter (which is the equivalent of a regular ten-mile run carrying a log) was swimming. This is probably the perfect exercise for someone expecting a baby, especially as it's something you can take the children you already have along to. Our local pool has a wave machine, which I adored, as it made me feel weightless for a few moments. Unfortunately, one afternoon I was swept away and rolled over a man lurking in the shadows in a pair of hot-pink Bermudas. When he finally emerged with his nose running and his face purple it was apparent he thought he'd been hit either by a hippo or part of the ceiling.

I didn't go to any classes at all, mainly because I simply didn't have time for things which didn't also involve Fifi. Instead, we bought a copy of the Jane Fonda workout for pregnant women, which tackled hitherto unconquered regions of the anatomy but bored me rigid. Fifi and I tried Jane's exercises before school for about three days before giving up.

Moderate exercise throughout your pregnancy will help you to boost your body image at a time when it will receive a severe thumping, give you some much-needed energy, and also help you to get back into shape afterwards, since it is impossible to expect stretched muscles to return to fitness if they were never used beforehand. Exercising during pregnancy can help prevent back strain, varicose veins, the dreaded piles, and constipation. Never ever push yourself to the point of stress, however, and gentle exercise such as stretching classes or swimming is to be preferred to anything which involves jolting you, such as high-impact aerobics.

Walking and swimming for at least thirty minutes three times a week seems a reasonable amount of exercise to aim at. Most sports are safe, but there are a few to avoid: all contact sports, water-skiing, diving or jumping into the water. This can force water into the vagina and is dangerous. Avoid any sport that requires good balance, such as gymnastics, riding, or speed cycling, because your stomach will make you more prone to fall forwards. Avoid scuba diving, too, because the unborn baby is susceptible to decompression sickness.

Be sure to get your doctor's OK for any exercises you are doing, especially when it comes to exercising on your back in the last six months of pregnancy.

Your back Towards the middle of the last month, I found myself being plagued by back troubles. Every time I got down I couldn't get up again and had to walk around for ten minutes like a shift worker from a paddy field. The pain was appalling and I had to find some good exercises to relieve it. Back problems during pregnancy should never be ignored. With back pain, you should be extra careful lifting your other children up – it's better to bend down to give them cuddles.

Another thing you may find helpful when you're trying to rest is to lie on your side with a pillow between your legs, which seems to relieve some of the weight and stops you having that sensation that your stomach is about to fall off the edge of your bed, dragging you, your husband and all the bedclothes with it. Another excellent backache easer is to lie on your back, preferably on the floor, with a small cushion under your head. First relax your whole body and then gently do a pelvic tilt, and press your back into the floor. Take deep breaths and on each out-breath relax into the floor.

One of the causes of backache is poor tummy muscles. During my pregnancy, I found it hard to remember what a tummy muscle was, but swimming each day even for an hour makes a massive difference, not only when you're expecting your baby but during the labour – and afterwards, when you are trying to get back into your old clothes.

Your stomach There are a few exercises that strengthen poor muscle tone in the stomach which are bearable to do even when you don't feel like doing sit-ups! Lie on your back with your knees bent and your legs hip-width apart. Support your head and shoulders on two pillows. Place the fingers of one hand on your lower tummy. Breathe in. As you breathe out, tuck in your chin and slowly lift your head and shoulders. To further strengthen the muscles, lift your head and shoulders, as before, but keep your arms crossed on your tummy to support it and pull it towards the centre as you curl up. If it begins to bulge out from beneath your arms, you've come up too far. It's best to be very careful and gentle. Breathe in as you lower your head to the floor. Repeat three times, twice a day.

Your bosom This is likely to have become much larger and heavier during your pregnancy. You should wear a special bra throughout your pregnancy as there are no muscles to support the breasts themselves. There are certain exercises which do help to tone them. Do them naked and you will see the muscles tightening (and probably depress yourself at the same time). Make a loose fist with one hand and clasp it with the other. Hold your hands at breast-level and press them against each other strongly for a few moments. Repeat at eye-level and then at waist-level.

Your legs Unless your legs have always been very strong and you have been used to exercising, swimming and walking, you will probably find that the extra weight you're carrying will make them very tired. Strong muscles help to prevent cramp and also encourage your blood to circulate, which makes you less likely to develop varicose veins.

Gentle exercise like swimming and walking will help a great deal. Never sit with your legs crossed, and sit or lie with your feet up when you get the opportunity. Kick off your shoes and rotate your ankles as often as possible to boost circulation. Go shoeless, preferably barefoot, as much as you can, and wear support tights with Lycra. Don't stand up for hours on end.

Preparing for labour There are a couple of key positions, and they are both done on the floor. It's a good idea to try to practise each of them every day. For both of these it is important that your back is straight, as the straightening motion strengthens the back. Pain is always a danger signal. If you find holding any position a strain, stop it.

The first position loosens the hips, groin and pelvic area. It also gets your thigh muscles to relax and stretch. Sit on the floor with the soles of your feet together, hold your ankles or clasp your toes, then feel the stretch in your thighs and hips.

The second position is good for stretching the inside thighs, legs and groin and it also helps your legs cope with the extra weight. Sit on the floor with your legs apart and stretch them out so that the backs of your knees touch the floor; then push heels forwards with your toes up so that the backs of your legs stretch and the fronts of your thighs tighten.

Tone your childbirth muscle Although many women nowadays go to the gym or the aerobics class, one area of their anatomy is probably being ignored. It is their internal pelvic muscle, which supports the sexual organs and helps push a baby out. The technical name for this muscle is the pubococcygeus, but since everyone has trouble saying it, it is referred to normally as the PC muscle. Although several muscles actually make up the whole group, they are almost always used simultaneously. Some cultures teach the women to use their PC muscles as a matter of course. Middle Eastern dancers, for example, are taught to isolate many groups of muscles. When training to be a belly dancer, the woman learns to identify the muscles in and around her pelvis, in order to move them independently of each other and of the rest of the body. These dancers even learn to use one set of stomach muscles while keeping others still.

However, I'm not expecting you to learn to do that. The first thing to do is to locate your muscle, let alone learn to wiggle it. In the early Forties, a pioneering gynaecologist called Arnold Keigel gave the PC muscle the attention it deserved. It has been widely assumed that a weak set of PC muscles is the result of childbirth trauma, but today many experts believe that weak muscles can *cause* childbirth problems and are now prescribing pre-natal exercising.

Have you ever leaked a small amount of urine under stress (or hysterical laughter)? Do you have difficulty reaching orgasm? – that could be another indication of muscle weakness. If you are bothered by lower-back pain, frequent vaginal infections, pain on penetration, the problem may be chronic pelvic tension. Likewise, if you suffer severe menstrual cramps or have a weight problem. But ask your partner – he will tell you if you can intentionally contract your PC muscle during intercourse, or if you feel very snug, which will rule out PC weakness. If, however, your partner says he cannot feel much contact, you can suspect a weak PC muscle.

It is relatively easy to identify one's PC muscle by inserting a finger into the vagina and then alternately contracting and relaxing by squeezing, as if you were stopping a stream of urine. Although your vaginal walls are relatively uniform, your finger should be able to detect the PC muscle beneath the surface about 1in from the entrance. After using the one-finger, try using the two-finger test. Insert two fingers side-by-side as deep as you can with comfort, and then spread your fingers apart as if opening a pair of scissors. Now, by contracting your PC muscle, try to force your fingers back together. Another good method of identifying the PC muscle is simply to interrupt the flow of urine. If you can stop and start the flow of urine with precision, there is nothing to worry about – but don't worry; learning to contract the right muscle is part of the exercise.

To strengthen the muscle, squeeze it for three seconds and then relax it for the same amount of time. Do this ten times in a row; as you build up strength and endurance, increase the number of seconds until you have worked up to ten. Do not skip the equal period of relaxation, as that is as important as the contraction. At first, you may find that it is difficult to tell if you are contracting or relaxing, but it will become easier. You should aim at doing a hundred contractions at a time and about three hundred a day. These exercises can be done while watching TV, standing in the queue at Sainsbury's, sitting on the bus or at work.

Coping with Stress – Aromatherapy

Aromatherapy is the use of glorious distilled fragrances – the essential oils of flowers and plants, such as jasmine, gardenia and vanilla. The belief is that these fragrant oils contain deeply therapeutic qualities, helping us to feel more alert, relaxed, sensuous, or even, in the case of vanilla, transporting us back to childhood. Whether or not you discover during your pregnancy that a few drops of vanilla in your bathtub make you drift back to the nirvana of the eleven-plus remains to be seen, but no one can argue that soaking yourself in delicious waters, or rubbing yourself afterwards with delicately scented oils, will not help you feel relaxed.

Switch off horrible Radio One, switch on wafting violins and forget about the ironing... You might even consider investing in a small aromatherapy burner, a little plug-in hotplate, to fill the whole house with heady calming aromas. I do have to mention here that it's a good idea to tell your partner that you are about to transform your home into a womb-like casbah. When I first tried aromatherapy my husband came home, leaned his head against the front door, inhaled deeply and then said that something in the neighbour's skip must have gone off because there was a smell everywhere that was making him bilious.

Massage for you The aromatherapist will advise you over your selection of oils and their purpose. A combination of oils is then mixed into a base oil, which is usually sweet almonds or grapeseed. The function of the base oil is to aid absorption into your skin and circulation. Take heed of the therapist's advice, as certain oils are dangerous when applied during pregnancy. Vertain oil is thought to stimulate a woman's periods, and should be avoided by mothers-to-be. Better to be extremely safe than sorry. The following oils are toxic and therefore dangerous to use while pregnant: wormseed, sage, basil, hyssop, pennyroyal, cedarwood, thyme, origanum, myrrh, cinnamon bark. Others are unsuitable for young babies, so be very careful in your selection.

The safest oils to use in the first three or four months of pregnancy are melissa mandarin, ylang ylang, bergamot (which I have to confess smells very powerful) and camomile. For massage use three drops of essential oil for every 10ml of base oil. After four months you can become more adventurous and try sandalwood; frankincense; rose; or mandarin, neroli and lavender blended up together in a heady mix that will almost asphyxiate men at twenty paces.

Try to prevail upon your partner to concentrate the massage on your feet, legs, swollen ankles, face, head, and shoulders. (Your lower back, which is often the site of throbbing lumbago-style aches, should be avoided by enthusiastic amateurs just in from the office.) What could be a more peaceful and sensuous activity for couples awaiting a birth?

Massage for baby When the baby arrives, don't stop your aromatherapy sessions. She can join you, too, especially when she's feeling tired and fractious. One drop of lavender and one drop of camomile in 20ml of your base oil makes a perfect baby mixture. (Mineral-based oils have a drying effect on a baby's skin, so avoid them.) Massage your baby gently, building up a steady rhythm all over her body. Continuous strokes along the spine will encourage her to fall asleep. Downward strokes are more restful, and upward strokes more invigorating. And don't forget her little feet. I always try to avoid getting oil near a baby's face as the skin here is so delicate, and it's also extremely important to keep oil away from a baby's eyes, but she will adore having her head and scalp rubbed.

Note Never drink oils. Never use undiluted essential oil on you or your baby.

Aromatherapy in the bath To calm down anxious fathers: four drops of clary sage, five drops of sandalwood, and five drops of ylang ylang.
   For cross babies: one drop of camomile and one of lavender.
   For your tired legs and feet: three drops each lemon, lavender and rosemary added to 50ml almond base oil.
   For healing you up after the birth: add to the bath water (or a large bowl of water) four drops each of cypress, camomile and lavender and sit in the water for ten minutes. This will soothe a sore bum enormously . . .

If you find that making up your own oil mixtures is daunting and expensive, ready-made aromatherapy oils are now sold in the larger high street chemists.

For help in finding your local aromatherapist, contact the *International Federation of Aromatherapists*, 4 Eastmearn Road, London S E 2 1 8HA.

Getting the Best from Your Changing Appearance

One of the first things that you'll be aware of in earliest pregnancy is the change in your body – and with the changes you may find a sudden and unexpected surge in modesty – and also find yourself on a bewildering see-saw of sexuality. One minute you're Hedy Lamarr and the next minute you'll feel about as sexually alluring as a newt's penis.
   In the past I'd always gaze agog at those girls who merrily strip down to a greying bra and those mystifying knickers worn over their tights in Miss Selfridge's communal changing rooms. I went in there recently to try on a puce cheesecloth smock that I was convinced would 'do', and the presence of my triple D cup Cross-My-Heart bra coupled with a faded maternity corselette made the most brazen of us feel sheepish.

Trying on the smock I displayed an almost Olga Korbut-like athleti-
cism. I wriggled around like those big fat women who you see on
Whitley Bay beach changing into a bikini under a floral hand towel,
and getting enough sand up their bottoms in the process to pebbledash
Centrepoint.

You're likely to find that normal standards of behaviour between
you and your partner go down the drain. A horrible lack of romance
can creep in, and suddenly you begin to wonder if all husbands are
like him. I can assure you now that whatever state his wife's in no man
will hoover the stairs or clean the bath, and that all men leave soggy
tea-bags on the side of the sink, have to be thanked if they make the
bed, make a noise like an exploding lilo when Victoria Principal is on
the TV, and read 3-D *Men Only* in bed when you're feeling like a
walking talking Goodyear blimp.

On the other hand, there are two very good things about fathers-to-
be which are always worth bearing in mind. The first is that they never
mind being woken up in bed with requests for a big gherkin, whereas
most men woken up at four in the morning by their girlfriends begging
for a big gherkin would think they were in big trouble. The other
wonderful thing is that he will not be seeing you with your eyes (thank
God). Your partner will be seeing you as a symbol of spring, a veritable
maypole of fertility, rather than the fat pig with no clothes that fit that
you imagine you have become in the last few months.

I think it's best not to draw too much attention to all these flaws he's
conveniently not seeing, blinded by love. Do not wake up in the
morning muttering self-indulgently, *God, I'm so gross, how can you
bear to go near me? You're sick, you are*, etc, etc, before he's even
sniffed the paper or nibbled the toast. Remember, give it another few
weeks and he'll be seeing sights no one prepared him for, like you
trying to get your tights on . . .

Try not to fall into too relaxed a state where, instead of doing sexy
dances around the TV, stepping over his carburettor in the process,
you're lying in bed all day eating dripping sandwiches, and wearing a
Waitrose carrier bag on your head to warm up the Henna Treatment Wax. You are the goddess he has placed on a pedestal; he didn't
place you lying in three inches of murky luke-warm water with
little hairs floating on the surface while you shave your legs in front
of him.

Always try instead to remember your newly acquired good points:
think of yourself as having a skin kissed by moonlight rather than the

colour of a dead trout, a bosom as firm as a ripe Gorgonzola, hair that ripples and cascades with all the nutriments throbbing around your body. Remember your good points and his loins will no doubt heat up like a TV dinner . . .

Keeping Up Your Dress Sense

One of the things that is rarely mentioned about being pregnant is that although you won't actually need 'maternity clothes' until you are five or six months pregnant, nearly all women find that they start to put on weight straight away, so there is a hideous in-between stage where you just look fat but you don't look pregnant. It's at this point that you find yourself longing to protest to complete strangers in shops, I'm not really fat, I'm pregnant, and you also notice that, although your stomach definitely doesn't warrant a whimsical blue tent, neither do your trousers fit you any more. A pregnant woman's best friend is her safety pin.

After the fat stage has been struggled through, with you adapting your clothes as best you can and borrowing your partner's large white shirts and fishermen's sweaters, the next stage is even more of a challenge. There are two great problems with the maternity clothes currently available to women. The first one is that maternity 'fashions' manufacturers imagine that, as a woman's stomach increases, so her age magically decreases to the point where she longs to wear the same sort of dresses as Milly-Molly-Mandy. Large smocks fill the rails with Peter Pan collars, dropped hems, and fabrics printed with gambolling lambs against a lime-green background.

The alternative to this style is the trendy maternity shop, where a stick-thin assistant in Comme des Garçons advises you in a thick Gallic accent to wear black leggings with a Lycra tutu. Many women would not feel greatly drawn towards leggings and a Lycra tutu at the best of times – let alone with an extra three stone of weight on them. It is a hard time for the fashion-conscious. Fashion magazines always advise us not to hide our shape during pregnancy, but to flaunt it. I can tell you that by the end of your pregnancy it will be impossible *not* to flaunt it.

If you don't want to look a complete frump, stick to things that are as simple as possible when you buy them – i.e. clothes without ruffles, pussy-cat bows, pie-crusts, etc, and then add the kind of accessories that you've always liked. Often, maternity dresses come with heavily padded shoulders. When you're not pregnant, this has the effect of balancing larger-than-desired hips. When you are pregnant, they make you look exactly like a wardrobe.

You can go the route of 'borrowing' clothes from ex-pregnant girlfriends but this can make you feel uncomfortable – you wouldn't normally walk around in your friends' clothes, so set your own style. Try and do the whole thing as cheaply as possible because all pregnant women loathe their small wardrobe of maternity clothes with a passion by the end, and will want to make a funeral pyre of them. Having said that, it is a wise investment to have one party frock so that when you do get asked out you don't have to endure all the misery of being the only person there looking as though they just pulled up their tent-pegs and came as they were.

This is the one time when mail-order companies seem to come into their own. Most of the magazines for new parents have large sections of small adverts for companies doing maternity clothes with a little more thought behind them than can be found in many shops. A lot of them also do matching outfits for toddlers, or todgers, as my daughter calls them. I can only make a plea here that somebody will one day give me my own maternity range to design and rid the world for ever of orange corduroy dungarees. Since many people wear black almost all the time, it never ceases to amaze me that there has barely been a single black frock designed for pregnant women.

Happy Mother, Happy Baby

As your waistline expands and you feel the baby move, you may be wondering what it's like for her inside the womb. The loudest noise that a baby hears is the rhythmic pounding of her mother's heart and arteries. It's been discovered by obstetricians that playing back the mother's recorded heart beat to a crying newborn quietens her down and she will often fall straight to sleep.

The womb is extremely noisy during the last four months. Since the amniotic fluid, like water, conducts sound, the baby can hear her mother swallowing, her heart beat, and her blood circulation pulsations – all at a very loud, 72–84 decibels. This is extremely loud when you realise that normal speech is 65 decibels. The most distinguishable sound to the new baby is her mother's voice. This differs in pitch from all other sounds and blasts at the baby at 84 decibels. Newborn babies have been found to respond also to the theme songs of their mother's favourite soap operas.

Researchers have found that babies inside the womb get thrilled at the sound of pure musical tones. Their heart rates rise a full fifteen beats a minute for the first two minutes of a listening session. In one experiment, pregnant mothers during the last six weeks of pregnancy listened to their favourite classical music for ten minutes each day. The unborn babies immediately recognised this new stimulus. Unborn babies do not respond to monotonous single tones, even when played very loudly and only three feet away. They like proper music. In another experiment, doctors probed the negative effects of airport noise on the unborn. Researchers found that women who were living near landing strips gave birth to infants who were generally smaller, had lower body weights, and were more likely to be born prematurely.

New studies reveal that unborn babies begin sucking their fingers as early as eleven weeks, and, since their eyes are open at nineteen weeks, it is possible that a baby can see her hand and her environment while still in the womb.

Most research about babies before their birth, of course, looks at the baby/mother relationship, but there is increasing evidence that suggests fathers and their own response to the pregnancy have a huge impact on the baby's future life. Studies have found that women have happier and better pregnancies and birthing experiences if they have loving, understanding and responsive partners during their pregnancies. One study rated the quality of a woman's relationship with her partner only second in importance to her attitude to being a mother.

Another researcher found that a bad marriage or an unhappy relationship was one of the greatest causes of emotional or physical damage in the womb. On the basis of his study of over 1,300 children and their families, it was concluded that a woman in a bad, turbulent or violent marriage ran a much greater risk of producing a psychologically or physically damaged child at birth than a woman in a secure one. Even smoking, physical illnesses and truly hard physical labour seemed unlikely to exert such damage. Babies of poor marriages were found to be five times more jumpy and frightened than the babies of happy relationships, and these babies often grew up into problem children. Research found that at four and five years old, these children were under-sized, timid, and over-dependent on their mothers.

All of this has important implications. By creating an emotionally happy and safe environment in the womb, a mother is giving her child the best possible start in life. During this time, the mother's attitude is the baby's first experience of life in the world. Everything that she feels will affect the baby in one way or the other.

How we relate to our babies while they're in the womb – what they hear and what they sense – is vitally important. Sweet-talking is obviously preferable to shouting . . .

THE NINE MONTH CALENDAR

Four Weeks

Your baby From a single, microscopic fertilised egg, around twenty-five days after conception a tiny tube which will eventually become the heart begins to beat and circulate blood. At one month, the developing embryo is no bigger than a pea, but, to you and your husband, she's probably got a name, an entire personality, and possibly a wardrobe.

Your body A missed period may not have been the first indication that you were pregnant. Other signs could have included bigger breasts and morning sickness. And there are some women who just *know*, almost as soon as their partner has rolled over and gone to sleep. Uterus growth begins: the weight of your uterus will increase up to twenty times during the pregnancy.

Your feelings Don't be surprised if your initial feeling of awe and excitement suddenly become a little mixed with apprehension, along the lines of, How much will my life change when I am a mother?, or, I'm never going to have an Azzedine Alaïa dress now. Of course, your life will change completely when you're a mother, in a way that makes you forget what your life had been like before. You will find yourself wondering how on earth you had such fun before you had a baby. Talking your emotional see-saws out with a close friend or a partner is a good way to calm early pregnancy jitters.

Lifestyle changes Now's the time to stop smoking and drinking if you haven't already and also remember to avoid all contact with your pets' litter boxes throughout your pregnancy. Animal poo contains an organism which causes a very serious foetus-damaging disease called toxoplasmosis. You should also always wash your hands after stroking your pets, and thoroughly wash all fruit and vegetables, because the toxoplasmosis germs can be transferred to unwashed produce through the soil.

Eight Weeks

Your baby Your baby is now about 1in (2.5cm) long and weighs ¹/oz (4g). Her eyes, nose, arms and legs, are becoming more recognisable. A little face is forming. By the end of the second month, the arm and leg buds will have grown into limbs. The internal organs are rapidly taking shape.

Your body You may find that you're needing to go to the loo more, and, due to the hormonal changes, starting to feel unusually tired. Sneak in naps when you can and try to slow down. You can expect to feel more energetic when your hormone-changes level off at the end of the third month. Many pregnant women find that their hair-growth gets faster while at the same time their hair-loss slows down, giving the hair a new Farrah Fawcettness. Unfortunately at the same time you may find that your skin oils are increasing, which can cause spots. To minimise this, avoid heavy creams and be sure to drink at least eight glasses of water a day. Your breasts and uterus continue to increase in size.

Your feelings Swings in sexual mood are very common. Throughout your pregnancy, just talking to your husband or partner about how you feel will help stop him from feeling pushed out or rejected (or exhausted!).

Lifestyle changes Now is a good time, if you have health insurance, to check up on exactly how much your plan will contribute – if anything – towards bills incurred by your pregnancy. Also, if you work and want to continue doing so, make sure that you're clear about maternity and paternity leave.

Twelve Weeks

Your baby Well-defined genitalia develop. Ears, fingernails, toenails appear and tooth buds begin to sprout inside the dental arch. At three months, the unborn baby is about 3¼in (8cm) long and weighs about 1oz (28g). She can swallow and move her upper lip, which are the beginnings of her sucking reflex.

Your body Blood volume will be increasing steadily, which sparks one of pregnancy's best side-effects – the much-vaunted 'glow', although I simply looked red in the face. Because of this extra blood volume, you may find that your gums are swelling and/or bleeding. Perspiration

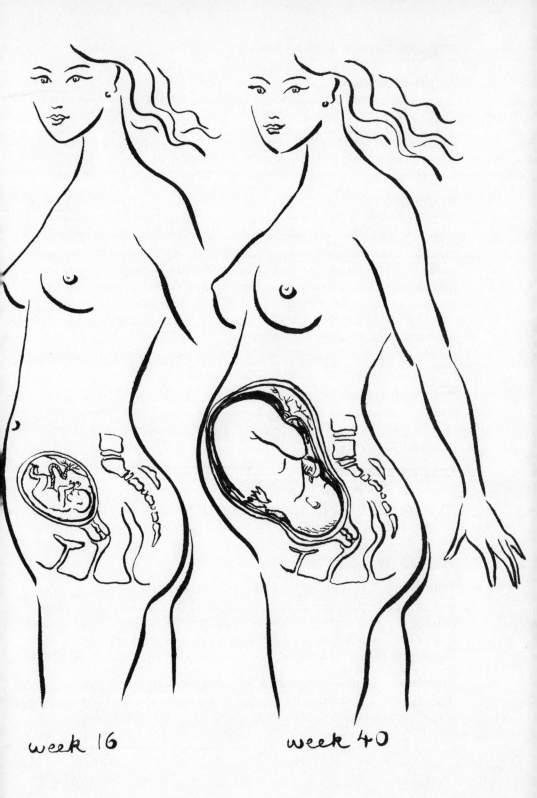

week 16   week 40

and vaginal discharges increase, but if itching, burning or pain accompanies the discharge, see your doctor. Your enlarged uterus begins to press on the pelvic leg veins. Fluid retention rises for some women, which may mean that your jewellery doesn't fit any more. Women need this added liquid for cell production, so don't cut back on drinks or salt. Any uncomfortable or very sudden swelling should be reported to your doctor.

Your feelings Weight gain may throw you into a miserable depression, especially if you're used to being slim. It's very difficult to adjust to suddenly having somebody else's body and not having any clothes to fit. There are two things that should cheer you up; you are not actually fat, but laden with baby-supporting tissue, and your body is doing its job well. And think positively at all times about how your body will re-shape up very quickly after the birth. Most women find that they lose at least a stone in the first week after the birth, and the rest in the six to nine months afterwards.

Lifestyle changes It's a good idea to clear out your wardrobe temporarily and leave only the things that actually fit. This will prevent you from throwing yourself into the wardrobe sobbing, clutching sequinned sheaths and ski pants in remembrance of waists past.

Sixteen Weeks

Your baby The baby now weighs about 5oz (142g), even though you are probably a fat heifer. Her organs are beginning to function, and she can swallow, suck her thumb and make a fist. You can feel content that you are already producing a genius. By four months, the baby is about 6in (15cm) long and has fully formed hands.

Your body Your approximate weight gain will be about 4lb (1.8kg), if you're lucky. You will start to feel more energetic and not so sick. Your breasts will be less sensitive and your stomach noticeably bigger. You may find that you are starting to get piles. Remember to stick to a high-fibre diet, avoid straining in the loo, and reduce pressure by lying down as frequently as possible. Having a maternity girdle does ease the weight problem.

Your feelings You may find that sex becomes more satisfying as your physical discomforts have passed. You may feel headily freed from either contraception needs or your conception efforts.

Lifestyle changes If you are employed, now is the time to discuss those maternity leave plans with your boss or supervisor. Be sure to iron out all these details well in advance, including the length of your leave, your pay and any work from home or part-time options available to you, which may become more attractive than you think. Nobody knows how they will really feel about returning to work until they've actually had a baby, so don't think that this is all written in stone and you can't change your mind later.

Twenty Weeks

Your baby Your little baby now has eyebrows, eyelashes, fingerprints and soft, downy hair all over, called lanugo (which sounds like some kind of diarrhoea remedy). She will be around 10in (25cm) long and weigh about 8oz (227g). You will soon start to feel elbow jabs and kicks. A woman expecting her second baby may discover that she has been feeling her moving around for some time already.

Your body A large, dark vertical line of pigment called the linea negra will probably appear from your belly button to your pubic hair. This starts to fade after you have the baby. Your nipples may start to get darker and could release colostrum, a watery, yellowy pre-milk. You may discover that stretch marks are starting to surface on your tummy, your thighs and your bosom. Although they may look fierce now, they do fade rapidly to a silvery thread. Try and counteract these as much as possible by rubbing in anything from olive oil to one of the specially prepared lotions available. I became a complete sucker for any claim made by any advertisement and bought myself a tub of green slime which smelt like something out of the rear end of a nocturnal animal. As time ran out, I rubbed and rubbed this pungent grease all over me, until we discovered it was affecting our dog's eyes, so I had to stop . . . You may find that you should stop wearing high-heels, as lower back pain starts to increase now.

Your feelings You will be experiencing constant nudges and kicks. This, combined with your very large tummy, will make you feel – probably for the first time – that you really are, definitely, pregnant and that there really is a baby there. This can actually come as something of a shock. I remember ringing my best friend, scared witless, and telling her, 'Oh, my God, I've suddenly realised, this baby's actually coming to live with us.' Now, of course, I am extremely happy that she did, but I did have a wobbly couple of days.

Lifestyle changes Start finding out about public transport options. You may find that it is difficult to fit behind your car steering wheel. Always remember to wear your seat belt. The pressure will not harm the baby. Buckle the belt below your belly, across your pelvis, and use a double-protection shoulder harness if possible.

Twenty-four Weeks

Your baby The baby is starting to get fatter now. She weighs around 1lb 2oz (500g) and is about 12in (30cm) long. The baby's breathing motions will have begun.

Your body Certain lovemaking positions may have become awkward or painful, as your stomach gets huge and the baby drops lower into the uterus. If you have apprehensions about sex harming your baby, don't; she is well protected and sealed in the amniotic sac. Ankles may swell due to your water retention. A good swelling soother is to lie on your back with your knees bent, place your hands under your right knee and clasp knee to chest, then circle the right foot five times to the left, five times to the right, and then repeat with the left foot. Repeat this several times a day. Your belly button may also pop out due to the internal pressure on it, but it will go back after delivery. You may find that sleeping is becoming uncomfortable because being on your back inhibits blood circulation. Try to sleep on your side.

Your feelings You may find that as you become more noticeably pregnant, so there is an increase in completely unsolicited advice. You will also notice that, although you are often the centre of attention because of the pregnancy, people are bizarrely unhelpful when it comes to a pregnant woman's obvious need for assistance in certain situations. During my last pregnancy, I frequently found myself standing in the street with ten bags of groceries and never once found anyone willing to lift them into a taxi. It's also nowadays very unusual for anyone to give their seat up on a bus. This can make you feel quite irritable, if not murderous. The best thing to do is ask – then people can't refuse.

Lifestyle changes It's a good idea at this point to tour the hospital you will be attending with your partner so that you are familiar with the surroundings.

Twenty-eight Weeks

Your baby Your baby is now around 14½in (37cm) long and weighs 2½lb (1kg approx). Her eyes can now see and her tongue can taste.

Your body Your tummy may begin to feel very itchy as your stomach stretches. If you find you develop prickly heat, as I did, an aloe lotion will help ease the discomfort greatly. Try to get up slowly as you may feel dizzy or faint if you rush around.

Your feelings As it gets nearer to the birth, women often worry intensely that there will be something wrong with the baby. Combat this by re-directing your thoughts whenever you find them wandering into distressing scenarios. Discuss with your doctor and midwife any fears that you have, as they will be in a position to put your mind greatly at ease.

Lifestyle changes It's a good idea, if you can, to take showers, not baths. It's easier now to lose your balance as you haul yourself like a walrus out of the bath. If you are due to travel anywhere, some airlines will now not take you if you look too close to delivery. By now you are already probably stocking up on baby basics – vests, nightgowns, nappies, baby soaps, bottles, steriliser (or hoarding some of the new, disposable bottles, which save time and energy). You should also now invest in a papoose. All babies love being carried round in one.

Thirty-two Weeks

Your baby She will now weigh around 4lb (1.8kg), and will be about 16in (40cm) long. She will have developed, through you, many of her antibodies.

Your body Especially if you are expecting your second baby, you may find that you are experiencing what are called Braxton Hicks contractions, which are basically tightenings of the uterus as it gets ready for labour. These can be very disconcerting in the middle of the supermarket, as you feel you're going into labour every time they happen. Any regular little spasms of your stomach are your baby getting hiccups.

Your feelings If you have been taking any natural childbirth courses, remember that natural childbirth doesn't necessarily equal success. Any other method that you may at the last minute decide on doesn't mean you've failed. Every labour is different and you have no way of knowing how you may feel until it all starts to happen.

Lifestyle changes Consider purchasing a rocking chair. The gentle rocking will soothe and comfort your baby and it will be a pleasant seat for breast-feeding. Start freezing meals and buying any frozen foods you're planning to use. Stock your freezer up for when you come home with the baby. That way you won't endure the guilt of a hungry partner, the misery of a hungry you and the general feeling of disorganisation and chaos that is to be avoided at all costs. Now is the best time to work out your arrangements with your partner, your mother, your best friend, or maybe even a hired nurse or cleaner who can help you out during that first couple of months settling in after the birth.

Thirty-six Weeks

Your baby She is now about 17½in (44cm) long and weighs around 5½lb (2.5kg). The downy hair on her skin is starting to go, but her skin will be covered with a fatty substance.

Your body Your stomach pressure eases as the baby's head settles into your pelvis.

Your feelings Now is the time to distract yourself as much as possible, as you will be getting more and more impatient. You long for your baby to come so that you can start building a relationship with her. You are likely to feel tired, irritable, fat and fed up.

Lifestyle changes Most women discover that they get an incredibly strong urge to nest at the end of pregnancy. Don't be amazed if you find yourself desperate to clear out closets and tackle the most unpleasant domestic chores. Many women either decide to move completely, or possibly even worse, they get the builders in. Having the builders in, as we did, during a pregnancy, is enough to kill anyone, as they turned our entire basement into an intriguing re-creation of the trenches in 1914 and then proceeded to spend four months sitting on the rubble reading magazines.

Forty Weeks

Your baby She has reached full term and will be around 20in (50cm long) and weigh about 7½lb (3.4kg).

Your body You'll be alert to signs of the start of labour, like your waters breaking, the appearance of the 'show', or the beginnings of contractions.

Your feelings You'll be in a constant state of anticipation – try to relax and not get too agitated.

Lifestyle changes Don't forget to buy film and make sure your camera works. You will want to record those first, fragrant moments of your baby's life. Start packing for the hospital: the essentials are at least two nighties, underwear, sanitary napkins, a fresh going-home outfit, shampoo, conditioner, toothbrush, toothpaste, make-up, Walkman, tapes, magazines, Evian spray, a list of telephone numbers of friends and a large supply of 10ps or a phone card.

SECOND BABIES

If you are expecting your second baby, there are a few points to remember to help your first child get used to the idea of a new addition to the family with ease.

Hospital Your child may never have been separated from you, so make sure that she knows exactly who will be looking after her for the duration of your stay. It's also a good idea for this friend or relation to spend some time with the child, near to the event, so that she feels happy and secure with them.

Breaking the news It's hard to know when the best time is to tell a young child there's another on the way, as they have a very poor concept of time – in fact, none at all. As soon as the baby starts to become a visible bump, broach the subject with a smaller child. For an older child – upwards of four – you could tell them any time, but link it to some landmark such as Christmas or a family birthday so they have an idea how long the wait is going to be. Also, be prepared to be bombarded with endless questions in the middle of supermarkets and bus queues. Fifi asked me if my waters had broken in a 400 decibel voice in the changing room in Chanel.

Talking about babies When I was expecting Peaches, Fifi and I found the topic of sex coming up constantly in our conversations. Fifi asked me how her father and I had decided to have a baby and what we had to do to arrange it in a quite astonishingly loud voice in the middle of the Natural History Museum. Several museum attendants craned forward in anticipation as I explained to Fifi all about the 'special cuddles' involved in getting a new baby. At the end of my lengthy and passionate description, she asked me if, next time I was doing it, I could give her a yell so she could come in and watch because she still couldn't quite understand how any Daddy's could do so many things. We moved on to another mammoth. There was a long pause. Fifi turned to me and said in a piercing whisper, 'So, these sperms you've told me about, what do they do all day – argue?'

Your child will be intensely curious – not only about how the baby got there in the first place, but about what the baby will be like when she comes. Now is a good time to explain that newborn babies actually don't do much at all except drink milk and sleep. Although it sounds obvious, a small child won't realise that a baby can't sit up, play, gurgle or wave a rattle around until at least four months. Your child probably expects an instant playmate and talking will prevent disappointment. When Peaches was a month old, Fifi turned round and said, 'Mummy, I do love Peaches, but she's very boring. Why couldn't we have had a donkey instead?'

Young children love hearing about their own birth and what they were like as babies, and it is important now to start emphasising how completely wonderful and beautiful they were, and how you hope that the new baby will be just as gorgeous. Young children are hugely flattered by the thought of their younger siblings copying them and emulating their startling perfections.

Include your child Share the forthcoming events by letting your children come with you to doctor's appointments, especially to see the scan of the new baby and to hear her heart beat. As you start making preparations for the hospital, let your child help with things like packing your bag. If you'd like your child to be present at the birth, find out if the hospital is amenable.

Braxton Hicks contractions These happened so frequently towards the end of my second pregnancy I was led to believe the baby's arrival was imminent virtually every day for about six weeks. I hovered in a constant state of anticipation, re-packing my three nighties in the fifteen-minute gaps between meals and trips to the loo. In the end I decided that I was going to use this month as an exercise in self-improvement and positive thinking – two things I rarely indulge in.

The first thing I did was enrol for driving lessons. This was because the prospect of manoeuvring a pushchair, a five year old, and various carrier bags containing the skintight sheaths I imagined myself to be wearing ten minutes after the birth became rather daunting. I decided that I'd take a crash course. There's only one problem with driving at the end of a pregnancy – I virtually had to sit in the back seat to make room for my stomach behind the wheel.

On that first lesson I was so nervous that I started to have wild contractions as we raced up the Embankment at 13 mph, the instructor's toupee flattened against the back window by the powerful G-forces of my Ford Fiesta. When we finally swerved to a halt at the traffic lights outside the Houses of Parliament, we both felt totally drained and had to go for a Big Mac round the corner to recover.

As we rapidly approached the date set for my practice test, I noticed that my instructor was a shadow of his former self. He battled on as I attempted to master the art of the eight- and seven-point turn and reversing around a corner. None of these is easy if you find that while pregnant you totally forget which is left and which is right. My instructor finally broke the news to me after I did a three-point turn straight into an oncoming milk float on the other side of the road that it was the belief of the Quickfire Driving School that I should postpone my test until after the baby had been born.

The next thing I did, which I would recommend to anyone who can find the time and finance for this sort of wild, extravagant, Liz Taylor-style behaviour, was to book myself into the hairdresser twice a week, working on the principle that anyone will feel better after they've had their hair done, even if the rest of you looks like Orca.

TWINS

Detection Only thirty years ago, more than 70 per cent of twins went undetected until the moment of birth, which must have caused many fathers to develop quite runny bottoms. Now, this doesn't happen very often because of sophisticated ultrasound techniques which can detect twins as early as five weeks. Doctors don't usually break the news until the end of the third month because in one in five cases one of the twins is reabsorbed into the body without any complications.

Incidence In this country, the average is one set of twins for every hundred pregnancies, although this is increasing all the time because of the use of fertility drugs. Oddly enough, in some countries there are more twins than others, although it's not known why. In Finland, for example, twice as many twins are born as in West Germany.

Characteristics About three-quarters of all twins are non-identical, which means that their mother released two eggs at the same time. These eggs were fertilised by two different sperm cells. The tendency to release two eggs per monthly cycle is thought to be hereditary. These brothers and sisters don't look any more alike than children born singly in a family. Identical twins, on the other hand, develop from one egg which divides into two separate cells shortly after being fertilised by a single sperm. These babies look exactly alike, are always of the same sex, and often even their own mother can't tell them apart.

Extra care during pregnancy Women expecting twins look pregnant much earlier on: their bump is clearly visible by twelve weeks, and by twenty-eight weeks they are as big as singly pregnant women at full term. A lot of care is needed to ensure that two little babies grow as happily as one in a place that was really only designed for a single occupant.

The mother of twins will be affected by double the amount of hormones floating around, and this can cause severe morning sickness. She is likely to develop worse stretch marks because it's hard not to put on weight. She also has to put up with a great deal of kicking around inside her from very early on. Sometimes the cervix will begin to open too soon because of the heavy pressure from two babies, and a stitch will have to be put in to keep the babies secure.

Complications at birth One third of twin pregnancies go into premature labour – most of these three or four weeks early. Only 8 per cent of twins are born before the thirtieth week. If you're expecting twins, make sure you arrange to have them in hospital with all the latest technology at your disposal. Caesareans are also more common with twins, often because both babies are lying in the breech position or the leading twin is lying across the cervix.

It's a good idea, while you're still pregnant, to join a twins club so that you can get a foretaste of life with twins and pick up some helpful hints. Or you might want to join *The Twins and Multiple Births Association*, 292 Valley Road, Lillington, Leamington Spa, Warwickshire CV32 7VE.
For further support and advice, contact *The Multiple Births Foundation*, c/o Dr Elizabeth Bryan, Queen Charlotte's Hospital, Goldhawk Road, London W6 0XG.

Chapter Three

The

Happiest Day

of

Your Life

The day my daughter Peaches was due to be born I was determined that her time was up and she was going to make her appearance. So I cleaned the entire house. We have a bright red industrial Hoover which actually needs a trained lumberjack to lift it and I hauled it up and down the stairs, tossing rugs into the air and doing origami with them. I polished, I cleaned, I bathed our horrid little dog. Then I went swimming and ploughed up and down for quite a while until, unable to take the stress any longer, my swimsuit ripped up one side.

When I got home we were meant to go to a première, but I couldn't have gone anywhere, I was so tired. Nobly, I told Bob to go out and I got into bed with Fifi for a cuddle. It turned out to be rather a long cuddle. It started at nine o'clock and by ten I'd seized up completely and couldn't move.

I lay there, bathed in the glow of her Yogi Bear nightlight, convinced I'd given myself a hernia carrying the monster turbo-carpet-smacking Hoover up eight flights of stairs. When Bob got home he was unfortunately accompanied by a rabble of giggling girls and their escorts. I heard Pamela Stephenson remarking that I must be huge by now. Huge, I thought miserably, and unable to move.

Bob came upstairs and tried to haul me up like he'd seen in an episode of *The Professionals* about ten years ago, which nearly killed both of us. In that sensitive and understanding way beloved of all husbands he let go of me, breaking the bed and several floorboards in the process, and went off to make everyone a cup of tea. 'Don't worry,' I called weakly down the stairs. 'I'll be all right.' It still hadn't dawned on me that I was in labour, which just goes to show you're not that much cleverer about the whole process the second time.

Fifi got up, beside herself with excitement about going out at one in the morning. Bob got us all in the car and then realised he wasn't sure where the hospital was.

One thought occurred to me when we'd finally got to the hospital and Bob told me that my doctor, the Warren Beatty of medicine, was on his way. It was that yet again I'd been taken by surprise by the whole event.

Having virtually swum the Channel the day before, then collapsed into bed, my hair had dried into a style that was a cross between something that gets hung from the altar at Harvest Festival and a Brillo pad. Not that I wish to appear vain. It was just that I kept thinking about all those photos we'd take after the baby was born and, in years to come, I imagined her asking me why I'd worn a Shredded Wheat on my head when I had her.

'Call my hairdresser,' I said out of the corner of my mouth, so that the midwife didn't hear. I was told it was three in the morning and not the best time to grapple trend-setting teasy-weasies out of their L'Uomo Vogue lift-and-separate pyjamas. So instead, Fifi and I settled into the two single beds we'd pushed together in our room, then fell into the fitful sleep of those awaiting a big event.

The day in hospital seems to start about ten minutes after the last one ended. No sooner had I had my breakfast, which was an ancient recipe for porridge handed down from the last days of the Bastille, than my hairdresser Nicky arrived complete with his assistant and a cloud of glamour. He plugged in his Carmen rollers next to the foetal heart monitor and started furiously tugging at my hair, which had shrunk about three inches in the night. Several nurses came into the room to have a look at what was going on. Nicky shoved Carmen rollers into everyone's hair, so they had to stay there, because it's hard to have an air of calm authority with a large, pink foam curler stuck in your fringe.

Then my devilishly attractive doctor arrived and drily commented that he was delighted the labour was progressing so well. I lay back thinking he was just like one of those heroes in books called *When Hearts Cascade*, with square jaws and dark, brooding souls. Having been seen with my hair in curlers and my legs in stirrups, it is hardly likely I'll ever see this tempestuous side of him, though.

After he'd left, I realised that something in my drip was definitely disagreeing with the large quantity of grapes and chocolate which Fifi and I had consumed after breakfast. I had to ask everyone else to leave then while I threw up. I wished I was truly glamorous like Zsa Zsa Gabor, who I'm sure never throws up while she's having her hair done.

Fifi was present while her new sister was born. She was a very active participant, standing on a chair next to the bed, shouting, 'Push, push,

push,' like a very small cox in the Oxford and Cambridge Boat Race. She mainly wanted me to hurry so that she could eat the mint which had fallen down the side of the bed. I felt like I was definitely crossing the pain barrier.

'I feel like Ben Johnson,' I panted. 'Well, you're drugged up enough,' said Bob. 'Oh, every one a Maserati,' I snapped back like knicker elastic. 'Who's bought a Maserati?' asked my doctor, looking up from half-way under the bed . . . This illustrates the pointlessness of trying to hold conversations during labour.

Peaches was born, looking perfect and gorgeous, like a little peach. The doctor said it was a girl. Fifi fell off her chair, cheering, and came over to my bed. 'Can I have my mint now?' she asked . . .

LABOUR

When to Go Into Hospital

Even though I've had two babies, I'm still not sure how to pinpoint the onset of labour. Many mothers feel equally uncertain and delay going into hospital for fear they will cause everyone a lot of trouble for a false alarm. Generally speaking, as soon as you start to have regular contractions about every ten minutes, and this has been going on for more than an hour, you can assume you are in labour, even though your waters may not have broken. If they have, the baby is definitely on the way and you should go straight to the hospital. You may also have noticed a little period-like bleeding, the 'show', although this can appear several days before labour begins.

It is currently fashionable to suggest to mothers that they delay going into hospital for as long as possible by having tea, cleaning out cupboards, or wandering around the house. In general, however, I think it's wise to say that, especially with second babies, you should err on the side of caution and make your way to the hospital, as babies can come very quickly and surprise you at the end of the stairs.

The Three Stages of Labour

Labour is divided into three separate stages. The first is from the start of your labour until the time when the midwife tells you that your cervix is fully dilated, that is, when the cervix has opened up enough to let the baby's head through. The second stage is from the full dilation of the cervix up until the baby is born. The third stage is from the delivery of the baby until completion of delivery of the placenta, or afterbirth.

The average duration of labour is around twelve hours for a first

93

baby. However, I know someone who took an hour, and someone else who took thirty-six hours. There is no way of predicting how long it's going to take, although, interestingly, if your mother had an easy time, you are likely to have an easy time. This is not for any physical reason, doctors suggest, but because you have been influenced by your mother's attitude.

The first stage Sometimes women feel nervous about going into hospital, away from the security of home. If you feel baffled by any of the procedures or equipment, ask the hospital staff.

When you arrive at the admissions desk, give in your card which shows your hospital number. A midwife will then see you. She'll ask you whether your waters have broken, how often you're having contractions, and whether you are showing any blood. She will then take your temperature, blood pressure, feel your tummy, and listen to the baby's heart beat. Most hospitals will not, now, shave off your pubic hair, but they will give you a suppository to make you go to the loo. You must use this, as the last thing you want in your moment of glory is to poo over the baby (and your husband). The midwife or doctor will then give you a vaginal examination to see how far dilated you are and how far the baby's head has moved down. Every time you're examined from now on (usually every three hours) ask the doctor or midwife how far dilated you are, as it is greatly encouraging to know how you're progressing. You're fully dilated at 10cm, or five fingers' breadth.

You will stay in the first-stage labour ward until you're ready to deliver. You'll probably want to walk about, but try not to eat too much as you may throw up later – especially if you have an anaesthetic. For energy, try glucose tablets.

The second stage This may take place in the delivery room. Some hospitals use the same room throughout labour. By your bed, you will see a foetal heart monitor, which is used during the first stage, too. This records the baby's heart beat and looks for signs of foetal distress, either by means of an ultrasound pad placed on the mother's tummy, or by a tiny wire attached through the cervix on to the baby's scalp. These soundwaves go into the monitor, which records the heart rate by displaying a flashing light, or by writing a record on a long piece of graph paper, which you can later keep. There will also be an intravenous drip, should the need for a hormonal boost arise. The partograph is a simple chart that shows the whole progress of your labour: dilation; the location of the baby's head; the results of each examination.

At this point, you will experience your strongest and most painful contractions. To start with, the urge to push out will not be very evident, but, as the baby's head gets into the lower part of your vagina, it will become irresistible. You will probably (if you are having a traditional birth) be sitting propped up on the bed. During contractions, I've found it helpful to have my husband and midwife push hard against my feet while I pushed because it gave me extra resistance. When you can no longer hold your breath, let it out. Prepare to take another deep breath, and remember, don't push if you're not having a contraction as it uses up your strength. Your husband can become even more involved at this point by counting you through the pushes. Obviously, the aim is to push for as long as possible with as much force as you can muster. Do not be distressed if the midwife keeps listening to the baby's heart – it's normal practice.

Now you'll begin to feel the baby's head coming out. The midwife will make sure the baby doesn't shoot out, and will ease her on her way. As soon as the baby's head is free, her nose and mouth will be cleaned. If she has swallowed a great deal of liquid or mucus, it will be sucked out with a small, plastic tube. With the next contraction you will push gently once more and feel the rest of the baby's body slither out. Then your midwife or doctor will tell you if you have a little boy or girl.

The first few moments between you and your baby are vitally important. You should cradle the baby immediately on to your chest, and the two of you will have your first eye-to-eye contact. Then the cord will be cut, which will make it easier for you to cuddle your baby and get her on to your breast. However, with many babies, the air passages need a little more clearing out. To do this, the baby is put on a tiny platform, which is equipped with a sucker and some oxygen, in case the baby is a little blue – as often happens immediately after birth.

The third stage After the birth of the baby, the uterus contracts. In fact, as soon as the baby attaches herself to your breast, you will actually feel the uterus shrink. The placenta comes away from its attachments and is pushed out. It looks fairly unpleasant, rather like a massive uncooked haggis. In some cultures, people actually bake it in a pie as it's deemed to be full of nutrients, but personally I prefer hospital food, which is saying something. In some hospitals, the placenta is sent off for use in face-cream manufacture. Vaginal bleeding will continue for two or three weeks after delivery. By six weeks your uterus will have returned to normal size.

Small tears in the vaginal wall are quite common, especially during the birth of first babies. Many doctors feel it's better to make a tiny incision, called an episiotomy, than to allow the skin to tear jaggedly as the baby comes out. The stitches are put in straight after the third stage of labour and will drop off in a few days. In the meantime you'll feel pretty sore. Anything from two to ten stitches is quite usual. Episiotomies should not be performed without good reason; not all women agree that they should be standard practice. If you feel strongly about this, make sure you include it in your birth plan.

Pain Relief

Because of the increasing publicity surrounding natural childbirth and its growth in popularity, an unfortunate about-turn has happened. Now many women have started to feel guilt and a sense of failure if they have not enjoyed (or endured) a natural childbirth. It is important for women to try to regard labour as a time of choices, and not as some kind of competition as to who can withstand the most pain without 'giving in' to pain relief.

With both of my daughters, I had an epidural up until the last hour of labour, when it was then allowed to wind down so that I could push properly. In both cases, the anaesthetist travelled from Gerrards Cross and on the last occasion arrived wearing his pyjamas with a tailcoat over the top.

An epidural block This consists of an injection of a long-acting local anaesthetic that is put into the lower part of your back. This does not hurt. The tip of the needle is inserted into the spinal canal, close to the nerves that carry pain from the womb to the spinal cord above. In addition to not being able to feel anything in the middle, you also can't feel your legs, which is rather strange.

The catheter containing the anaesthetic remains in place throughout labour, but can be topped up or left off, as needs be. It gives a woman complete pain relief throughout labour, and is without question the most effective method available. A mother feels no pain at all, but at the same time is fully conscious and active throughout the birth. The disadvantage is that, occasionally, the lack of sensation can leave the mother not entirely aware of her contractions, so that she has to be told when to push, and this can lead to an increased need for a forceps delivery. Sometimes, mothers experience a fall in blood pressure which can make them feel faint or sick. I'd like to have my next epidural in the lift when I arrive.

Gas and oxygen (also known as gas and air) This is available in all hospitals. The gas should be breathed throughout contractions, but not between contractions or it will make the mother feel rather drowsy. It is used for the end of the first stage, and during the second stage, of labour. When the woman is in the second stage of labour, she should take only a couple of little breaths of gas, before holding her breath and pushing. It doesn't cause any harmful effects, but sometimes makes the woman feel slightly drunk. Our neighbour used rather a lot of gas and air during her last birth; while her son was being born, she was shouting, 'Oh my goodness, it's a lamb chop. I wanted a chicken!' – something she has quite understandably never lived down . . .

Pethidine This is the most common pain relieving drug. But it can, and does, cross the placenta and, having entered the baby's circulation, tends to depress her breathing. For this reason, pethidine is not usually given late in labour. As a mother, I am not sure about pethidine, as it does affect the baby at birth. It doesn't to me seem an ideal start to enter the world in a drugged state. There's plenty of time for her to worry about that later, at acid house parties.

Spinal anaesthetics These are often confused with epidurals, but the needle is stuck further in, into the spinal fluid. The muscle paralysis resulting from this is much more total, but lasts for only two or three hours and cannot be topped up. It can also result in a severe headache, which is no way to greet your new baby.

Natural childbirth This is (in theory, of course) a great idea. What could be more natural than keeping medical intervention to the minimum? We are all bombarded with stories about African women giving birth in fields while picking maize at the same time and balancing a basket on their heads. However, in Neasden, such mothers are comparatively uncommon. For many women, giving nature some help – which will, in turn, reduce her pain and exhaustion and increase the safety of both her and her baby – is not something to be smugly sneered at.

The late Dr Grantly Dick Read and Dr Lamaze in Paris pioneered the modern concepts of natural childbirth by advocating relaxation exercises which are based on careful breathing, which relieves pain. In Britain, the Natural Childbirth Trust teaches these classes, as well as other aspects of labour, with an emphasis on husbands attending with their wives and even breathing along with them. For some women who have learned these techniques, they are all that is needed to cope with a labour and delivery. And the sense of having given birth to your baby with very little help is probably similar to winning a gold medal in the Olympics. By the same token, any birth of any healthy baby with any amount of help is a success and a miracle, regardless of whether it was natural or assisted. What is most important is that, having been born, the baby comes into an atmosphere of joy and tranquillity, to be placed straight on her mother's heart in full view of the father. (And in our case, sisters, hairdressers and best friends. In fact, next time we're doing it with Harvey Goldsmith and selling tickets.)

A Few Thoughts on Having Dad Present at the Birth

New man finds himself feeling he has to attend the birth because if he doesn't it's tantamount to an admission that he really wants to head for the divorce courts. Not being there is what he secretly hankers after in the dead of night when he's feverishly practising his lamaze exercises and plotting the route to the cottage hospital. He pictures himself happily sitting on that chair in the corridor outside his wife's room, clutching a half-bottle of Newcastle Brown Ale and a handful of cigars ready to be informed of the birth of his new adorable baby, without having first witnessed the re-enactment of the Crimean War on a small single bed starring the woman he loves most in the world.

Nowadays it is almost impossible for a man not to attend the birth. No matter what, he's expected to be there, grey-faced and nervous, trying simultaneously to be supportive and not throw up into the foetal heart monitor when the going gets rough. In one wobbly hand he clutches the family polaroid, and in the other a moistened towelette to mop his wife's feverish brow. With every fibre of his being he's trying to avert his gaze from the lower half of the hospital bed.

Recently, even very famous pioneering childbirth experts like Michel Odent have doubted the usefulness of having husbands and boyfriends present because it's thought to slow the birth down.

Some fathers questioned in an American survey reported 'post-childbirth impotence' after watching their wives give birth. A friend of ours felt so unwell that he finally fainted from the sheer strain of it and had to be rushed to casualty for stitches after he cracked his head open on the gas and air canister by the bed.

The fashion for having fathers present started about twenty years ago. Women became aware that, sometimes when they were too far gone to argue, their birth plans went horribly awry. Doctors and midwives, perhaps too keen to whip up to the hospital canteen for a chicken korma, began hurrying things up to an alarming speed. So it seems that originally, at least, husbands were hauled in to be mediators ready to fight off anyone attempting to perform a quick sneaky episiotomy when Mum wasn't looking.

Things have now progressed; being spokesperson isn't enough, and jobs have had to be found for husbands weary of standing to attention at a loose end. Now they learn breathing exercises that leave them hyperventilating like wildebeests and wear green Wellington boots to make them feel more like Dr Kildare in his prime.

I've had my husband present at both of my children's births and wouldn't have liked it at all if he hadn't been there. I do suspect that both times he was praying he would develop raging Delhi belly and be forced to rush away from my side by the calls of nature. But it *is* a family event and I like having people around who can welcome a new baby with real love and interest.

Both times, though, he lacked that certain conversational *je ne sais quoi*. When I was having Fifi he leaned over the bed and whispered, 'Do you know your face goes completely black when you push?' which lacks the kind of back-to-nature romance I feel is needed at these events.

Labour Complications

Prolonged labour A very long labour is extremely tiring for the mother and can also be dangerous for the baby. If the labour seems to be going steadily, your doctor will take no action. But if you seem to be progressing abnormally slowly, your doctor will find out what is causing the delay. Sometimes it is due to weak uterine contractions, in which case an oxytocin drip may be introduced to strengthen them. Alternatively, your baby may be very big and the doctor may suggest a caesarean.

If you are already well into the second stage of labour, your doctor may perform a forceps delivery. Obstetric forceps are extremely light and fit around the baby's head. With them, the doctor gently lifts the baby out. A local anaesthetic is used, but occasionally a full anaesthetic is necessary. When a baby is delivered with forceps, little red marks or dents may appear on her face or head. These quickly fade and have usually disappeared a couple of days after the birth. Forceps deliveries are more common if a woman is having her first baby, or has had an epidural.

Vacuum extraction is the alternative to forceps; a small metal or silastic suction cap, which is attached to a little pump, is applied to your baby's head, which can now be guided through the entrance of the vagina, and delivery is completed normally. In some hospitals, this has replaced forceps, but it does have one disadvantage: it produces a round bruise on the baby's head where the suction pad was. But this fades in a couple of days.

Malpresentation The name for the normal position of a baby at birth is vertex presentation. But sometimes, babies are born in other positions and not head first. The most common form of malpresentation is breech, which means the bottom is coming first. About 40 per cent of breech births are delivered by caesarean but your labour can progress as normal, despite a breech presentation. Extra care is needed when the arms and the late-coming head are about to be delivered, and forceps will be used.

Foetal distress While you are in labour, your baby may suffer from a lack of oxygen. This occurs because the contractions of the uterus squeeze the placenta so tightly that it cannot carry enough oxygen-rich blood to the baby. It can also happen if the cord is being compressed or because the placenta is too small or not working well. A distressed baby's heart has either started to go very slowly, or extremely fast and irregularly. Sometimes, a distressed baby passes meconium (a sort of dark yellowy-green baby poo) from her bowel, which will come out with the amniotic fluid. But it's important to remember that meconium is not necessarily a sign of foetal distress – though its appearance is always noticed by midwives. If your baby *is* suffering from distress she must be delivered as quickly as possible which is likely to mean a caesarean unless you've fully dilated and vacuum or forceps delivery is possible.

Retained placenta Occasionally, the placenta is retained because it doesn't separate properly. A doctor may have to remove it manually under an epidural block or general anaesthetic.

Bleeding after delivery of the baby Postpartum haemorrhage is when blood-loss exceeds 1pt. This bleeding may be due to failure of the uterus to contract down firmly on the raw area left behind when the placenta separates. Normally, an injection is given to make the uterus contract. In some cases, a blood transfusion is necessary.

Caesarean section A caesarean means the baby is born through an incision in the mother's tummy into the uterus. Caesareans are often performed under general anaesthetic, but increasingly, an epidural is used so that the mother doesn't miss the big moment.

The cut is usually made beneath the bikini line, and is basically invisible once it has healed. Contrary to popular belief, the fact that you have had one caesarean does not necessarily mean that you cannot have a perfect, normal delivery next time. A mother who has had a caesarean may have to stay in hospital a little longer – for about seven to ten days – and will have the skin stitches or clips removed about five days after her operation.

After a caesarean you may feel a bit depressed. A lot of women somehow feel they've not done it 'properly' if they don't push the baby out themselves. This is a natural reaction, so don't worry too much; try talking to your health visitor to put your mind at rest. Remember, with birth there's no such thing as the right way.

If you're breast-feeding, it's a good idea to put a comfortable cushion over your scar so it doesn't get bumped about, and be careful leaping out of bed to get to the baby when she cries (if she isn't sleeping with you).

Premature birth A premature baby is one who usually weighs less than 5lb 8oz (2.5kg) at birth and is born before the thirty-seventh week of pregnancy. Multiple pregnancies and toxaemia are contributory factors to low birth-weight, as is a malfunctioning placenta. Smoking and stress can also make premature birth or low birth-weight more likely. A premature birth is always a great shock, and even more so when the baby is taken from you and put into a special care baby unit. One of my friends had her baby over a month early after a hard labour during which her boyfriend constantly told the midwife to get out of the way of his video camera, and my friend was then sick all over her long hair, none of which contributed to the feeling of spirituality and peace I'd harped on about for weeks beforehand. When her baby had to go into special care, it was the last straw.

Many premature babies face difficulties with breathing and feeding, and are more likely to have jaundice, and trouble with body temperature. Obviously, hospitals want to keep a close eye on them. But some doctors believe that a baby does better if kept close to her mother (unless the baby is very tiny indeed) rather than away from her in a special care unit. If, like my friend's, your baby has to go into an incubator, you should try to spend as much time as you can with her and do the routine jobs like washing her and changing her nappies. A tiny baby will greatly benefit from her mother being near by to stroke her and speak lovingly to her.

The methods of feeding your premature baby will vary considerably depending on how much she weighed in at birth. Breast milk is best because it contains so many antibodies which help the tiny baby to fight infections. Something I didn't know before my friend had her baby was that the breast milk of a mother with a premature baby is different and is exactly tailored to the baby's needs. Breast milk can be given by a dropper or by a very thin tube inserted in the baby's nose. Babies who are born before thirty-five weeks do not have their sucking and rooting reflexes and so cannot at first feed from the breast or the bottle. If you want to breast-feed, ask the nurse to help you put your baby on to the breast as early as possible, even if the sucking reflex hasn't yet started. Eventually, you'll stroke the baby's little cheek and she will turn to the breast, reaching for the nipple, and be able to suck instead of just licking. Once home from hospital, it may take your baby time to catch up with babies born at full term, but it won't be long before she does.

Nippers, Sam Segal Perinatal Unit, St Mary's Hospital, Praed Street, London W2 (071 725 0469).

Stillbirth This is when a mother gives birth to a dead baby. Less than five in every thousand births end like this. Stillbirth can be caused by toxaemia, premature separation of the placenta, severe abnormalities of the baby, and certain infections such as listeria, which is why it is so important to be alert to dangerous foods during pregnancy. Most commonly, it is because the placenta is not working properly and the baby has been deprived of nourishment.

Two of my closest girlfriends have experienced the tragedy of stillbirth, but they each handled the whole terrible experience in very different ways. One friend, together with her husband, held the baby afterwards and had photographs taken which they have treasured. By doing this the baby became a real person to them with a name and a burial place (even if your baby dies you will still have to register the stillbirth with the Register of Births, Marriages and Deaths; the hospital staff will assist you with all of this).

My other girlfriend was a single mother, who gave birth alone in a northern hospital. The baby was taken away immediately so that she never held or even saw him. The scars on her have taken years to heal: her absolute distress at never having held her baby or having had a chance to say goodbye have made her grieving much harder, especially as the hospital staff disposed of the body, so there was no funeral either.

A stillbirth is very hard to bear. The pregnancy and all the excitement and preparation for the previous nine months seem to have been such an utter waste of time. You are left with breasts full of milk, and a fat tummy, and nothing to show for any of it. Your love for the baby starts long before that child is actually born; many couples will have had a pet name for the baby; the mother has felt the baby moving inside her. You cannot expect to forget that in a few weeks, and it is a bitter, agonising blow which calls for massive support and love from friends and family. From my little experience of this, it seems important to accept that the baby was a real, proper child to her parents, and not keep saying things like, Oh, you'll soon have another one, as though the baby was a soufflé that went wrong.

Remember, too, that your other children will be affected, not only by the death of their future sibling, but also by your grief. The studies that have been done on this subject say that it is best to wait before you have another baby until you feel you have stopped mourning the lost child. This process also gives your body the time it needs to recover, just as you would have waited, had you given birth to a live baby.

The Stillbirth and Neonatal Death Society, 28 Portland Place, London W1N 3DE (071 436 5881).

YOUR BRILLIANT NEWBORN BABY

Is My Baby All Right?

General condition The apgar score is not a measurement of how brilliant your baby is going to be, so don't panic – but it is a measurement of her general physical condition immediately after birth. Marks from zero to two are given for each of the following – the heart rate, reflex, muscle tone, and respiratory effort. A baby who is in very good condition after her big journey is going to score a possible ten points – less than seven means that something might be wrong, and a score of less than four means that the baby's life is in danger because she is not breathing properly and needs assistance.

Some painkilling drugs used during birth can make it harder for your baby to breathe as they are passed from the mother's body into the baby's system. Other babies get short of oxygen while being born.

The head All newborn babies look as though they have heads that are rather large for their teeny-weeny bodies. A baby's head measures one quarter of her body length, whereas an adult's head measures only one-eighth. Some newborn babies have heads that look lumpy or even lopsided. These lumps are simply signs that her skull took some pressure in the birth canal. As the baby is coming out, the four large pieces of bone actually overlap. After a few days, this gradually goes back to normal. At this age, the bones in a baby's head are so soft that just lying down can slightly flatten one side of the head – temporarily. Caesarean babies escape any squidging and come out with perfect, unblemished heads.

Sometimes, a baby may show signs of the caput, a swelling of blood and fluid just under the scalp which disappears after two or three days. Even more alarming are the small fluid-filled lumps the size of table tennis balls that can also appear on a baby's head. For a few days, these lumps can grow slightly larger, but they disappear after a few weeks. They are caused by the mother's pelvis rubbing against the baby's head during labour.

The face Although, looking at your baby in that purely objective way that mothers have, you will see absolute perfection, you may notice a few patches on her face. The red patches on her eyelids are called 'angel's kisses' and they may even be on her back, too. Tiny blood vessels, they will fade within a year. The ones on her neck may take longer. I still have mine. Some adults – like me – have them under their hair.

Some babies also have what look like whiteheads around their noses. These little milk spots, as they are called, are caused by fat accumulating in the tiny glands under the skin. *Do not squeeze them*, however great the temptation. They will be gone in a couple of weeks.

Occasionally, babies have small red spots in their eyes. These disappear with no effect on the eyesight.

Cleft lip or palate This is when your baby is born with a hole in the roof of her mouth or a hare lip. Your baby will need surgery as soon as possible, otherwise feeding and sucking is difficult. A little later, the palate will be operated on. Initially, it is upsetting to see a baby with a cleft lip but now surgery is highly successful and the scars will be all but invisible.

Marks on the skin Although in photographs one never sees a baby with less than perfect skin, most babies really aren't born that way. Nearly all black babies and one in ten white babies are born with blue/ grey patches that look like large bruises on the bottom or on the back. These are a collection of skin colouring pigments that get less obvious as the skin darkens.

Fifi had a big red mark on her leg when she was born which I viewed with rather mixed feelings. On the one hand I didn't realise that the raised red marks are common and fade by the time the child is about two, but on the other I'd just seen a documentary about two women who'd left hospital with the wrong babies, so I was rather glad mine had a special mark so I couldn't confuse her with anyone else.

Fifi's birthmark was a strawberry naevus. Some of these marks enlarge over the months before they start to fade away. Anything you

think of having done to remove them will leave a scar, but left to their own devices they'll just vanish magically.

The worst and least common sort of birthmark is the port wine stain. This is flat and purple-coloured and does not fade away so easily. As children with these marks are sometimes teased and ignored at school, you may want to cover it up with special make-up. There are now laser techniques available which get rid of port wine stains almost without a trace, which is fantastic. So it's definitely worth consulting your doctor.

Jaundice Maybe your baby is yellow. She has probably got jaundice. To tell, look at her eyes – are the whites yellow? Your midwife will advise as to the best treatment. Usually, lying in the mild sunlight and drinking extra water will help flush out the yellow from her skin. If jaundice persists for longer than ten days, check with your GP. If it is serious, your baby will be treated in hospital.

Swelling Some baby girls – and baby boys – are born with bosoms. Their bodies are still in tune with your hormones and in a day or so, the swelling goes down. Girls may even bleed a little from their vaginas, which is normal. Some babies also have swelling around their belly buttons that gets bigger when they are crying and smaller when they are lying quietly. This doesn't hurt, but again, it's best to check with a doctor that it isn't an umbilical hernia.

The eyes Sometimes a baby will have eyes that seem to wander. This is because she has not built up the necessary muscles to control eye movement. But as the baby starts to focus, these muscles will get stronger and the squinting should have disappeared by six months. If the squinting fails to correct itself, your GP will refer you to an eye specialist. It's vital to get this fixed immediately. In past times, these squints were not dealt with until children were four or five, by which time the brain 'cuts off' the image from one eye and the child's sight can be impaired for ever. In most cases, proper squints are fixed by simple surgery with fabulous results.

Dribbling I must mention this because I am the mother of a family of dribblers. Most books say that dribbling starts with teething, but many mothers find that their babies dribble from the very beginning, at any excuse. The dribbling habit does pass but until then, put a bib on the baby and keep tissues handy. You may wish to buy shares in Sketchley's. Dribbling can lead to a sore chin. To prevent this, smooth on a little tiny bit of baby cream or zinc and castor oil cream on the delicate skin around your baby's mouth.

The Cleft Lip and Palate Association, Dental Department, Great Ormond Street Hospital for Sick Children, London WC1N 3JH.

The Joy of Bonding

Bonding should start the second your baby is born, and is the process by which the two of you fall in love. It is your time to woo your new baby into loving you, and the beginning of your love for her. It is nature's way of ensuring that babies survive: babies are genetically programmed to attract their mothers so that their needs are met. Not everyone agrees that this love is instantaneous. Critics quote the statistic that 40 per cent of women claimed in one survey that they didn't feel an immediate rush of love for the baby. No matter – I can't stress enough that by having your baby placed straight on to your breast at birth, and spending all your time with her at the hospital, the two of you will start to get to know each other and build up a loving feeling. Don't worry if it doesn't happen immediately, but don't give up, it will be worth all the trouble.

If your baby is born by caesarean, or for any reason has to be taken away from you at birth, do your utmost to minimise the time the two of you spend apart. Even if your baby is in an incubator, you can still cuddle her through the portholes in her little glass tank!

Sometimes during those first few days it might seem that your baby is being thoroughly disagreeable and you wonder how you'll ever cope, especially if she cries a lot or you have problems with breast-feeding. Try to give your baby still more love and cuddles, even when it might feel like she's rejecting you, and you'll pull through. I remember being dreadfully unhappy thinking Fifi didn't love me when she was only days old, but really it was because I was inexperienced in reading what she was telling me. So I'm very happy I had a supportive husband to help me persevere.

It's very hard when one's expectations of the new arrival have no basis in reality. Closeknit families and neighbourhoods are becoming a rarity, so our experiences of babies are more likely to come second-hand from TV, and we tend to imagine they are going to be like the winsome cherubs in loo roll adverts. Which of course is what they turn into but it takes a little time to get to know each other.

Many hospitals want to keep everything rather clean and tidy, and this is considered to be more important than emotional matters. Often, in the interests of other mothers and their need for sleep, newborn babies are taken away and put into a nursery. *Stand firm and let no one separate you from your new baby*, no matter what the nurses say. You've waited nine months to hold this baby and she's not going off on her own to a lonely place. Arrange for her to stay in bed with you, cuddled close, then you can start to learn what her different cries mean. Newborn babies are rapidly making their minds up what the strange new world is all about. It will seem a very cold, frightening place if she is whisked away from the only comfort she knows, your close proximity, her new skin thrust into an unexpected garment while she's desperate to communicate her needs to you. Babies separated from their mothers quickly begin to withdraw in order to protect themselves from the confusion they feel. It is hard to perceive the world as a new, friendly place if you are left to sob in a busy nursery, not knowing when you'll be taken back to Mum. Don't accept a sleeping tablet if it's offered, so that you can be alert to the baby's needs. It's important for both of you to have a little privacy together. Draw the curtains around your bed, ignore the rules as much as you can, and start to talk softly to your baby and stroke her. You'll be amazed how responsive and lovely she is.

Bonding isn't hard work, it's falling head over heels in love with a little bit of heaven on your doorstep, dressed in a pink or blue babygrow.

Chapter Four

Three

Months

That Can

Shake

the World

The first three months at home with your new baby may be surprisingly exhausting as you start to adapt to your new role. If you're sleeping with your baby, and holding her a lot, cradling her in a sling around your chest or hip, you are unlikely to be subjected to incessant crying. But it's still a big adjustment to make, because your baby will have a strong personality of her own which is hard to anticipate!

At first it's difficult to plan days, get everything done, and still get out of your nightie to go to the park or to meet up with a friend . . . But after a while you will fall into a routine, you and baby together. No longer will everything be done in slow motion like the Six Million Dollar Man catching a bus. I promise you this because I know that at first even the simplest trips can seem daunting. Just try and think of yourself and the baby as one person, and everything will start to get easier!

You'll also be adjusting to the new way that some people will be treating you, and if you are feeling at all sensitive, it can be quite disconcerting. I remember that when I had Fifi I somehow transmuted from what I rather imagined was a steaming sex siren into a dumpy person in smocks that people kept jokingly calling Mum.

By about five or six weeks old your baby will reward all your efforts at blowing raspberries, leaping up and down grinning inanely, chatting endlessly, by making a few sweet little noises in return. Peaches looked at me and said 'Goya' very loudly with a big smirk and from then on we've none of us had a moment's silence from her. Many mothers admit to feeling mildly silly chatting away to someone who can't really talk back. In the past, babies were always regarded as sort of lumps without feelings or emotions of their own, but EVERY little baby is a real person with a delicious personality waiting to blossom forth and greet you, and by endless chatting you are helping your baby learn to communicate. After all, you do want your baby to learn to talk eventually, even if it sometimes turns out to be embarrassing.

Everyone with a small child can tell you a hair-raising tale of the things that child has said in a very crowded room. When a friend of mine's child was about three she developed a great interest in nuns, because she'd been given a copy of *The Sound of Music* for her birthday. Hour after hour, the family was subjected to her renditions of 'Doe, a Deer . . .' and 'The Lonely Goatherd'. Finally, the friend took her to visit an aunt who was a nun, and lived in deepest Oxfordshire. The visit was extra special because the nuns came from a largely silent order. As the child launched into 'Doe, a Deer . . .' the nuns all gaily joined in. Suddenly the little girl paused. 'Mummy,' she said, 'what does massive mean?' My friend sighed with relief. 'Well, it means huge,' she replied. The child gazed up at the ceiling, looked around the red, scrubbed faces and continued. 'I thought it did, because you always say MASSIVE PENIS, don't you?'

It's almost impossible to imagine your little baby reaching these heights of verbal agility and humiliation as you sit there on the sofa at the end of the day with a greasy centre parting and puke on one shoulder.

LOOKING AFTER YOUR BABY

A newborn baby can see, focus and follow with her eyes – but only at a distance of about 10in (25cm). She can tell light from dark and also likes colours; she can turn her head to follow a face and after only two weeks will be able to identify your face and prefer it to all others. Even now, she will start to copy you and imitate your facial expressions. One of the most remarkable things about having a baby around the house is how sociable she is.

Very young babies don't enjoy sudden noises. What they do enjoy hearing is their mothers, fathers, sisters and brothers talking to them. For the first few weeks of her life, she is likely to sleep about eighteen hours out of the twenty-four, and spend the rest of the time feeding. Involve Dad in feeding times by encouraging him to wind the baby by gently stroking her back and patting it to get rid of any air she may have swallowed. During the first few days, all babies lose a little weight, after which they will regain their birthweight, then put on a steady 6–8oz (170–225g) per week. As long as your baby seems happy and content, and is putting on *some* weight, don't worry too much about precise amounts.

Getting Feeding Right

Breast or bottle? Breast milk is filled with goodness, and contains antibodies which will protect a young baby from illness. Breast-fed babies are less likely to get gastroenteritis and nappy rash. And breast-feeding has benefits for you, too, using up calories, getting your womb back into shape, and, if you are going to sleep with your baby, it's immensely convenient! Finally, as well as being so good for your baby's physical health, it is a bonding activity that you and your baby can enjoy, snuggling up close together.

Having said all of this, I've been something of a failure myself on the whole breast-feeding lark. Despite great intentions, both times I've

117

given up after less than three weeks. With Peaches I experienced real guilt about this, especially after I told my health visitor, who seemed to think giving up breast-feeding was similar to being a trainee child molester. But I was demented with pain and misery from the vast bosom I'd always dreamed of having. In the end the pain got the better of me, and we moved on to the bottle. If you do change to the bottle, *do not fret*. It is not the end of the world, your bonding is not destroyed for ever, nor will your baby develop a frightening host of ailments. However, I did make doubly sure that the baby's feeding times were a pleasant, cosy experience for her, holding her close against my bare skin while she had her bottles so that we didn't miss any valuable cuddling up times together.

How often should I feed her? A lot of new mothers are worried about the timing of feeds, having heard tales of women who feed their babies according to a strict timetable. A new baby doesn't understand that she'll have to wait, I'm afraid, so demand feeding is the only way to prevent the wails of a baby wondering where her next meal is coming from. In the early days most babies will want the breast about every couple of hours, although probably *your* baby will be completely different, just to confuse you! As she gets older she'll start to have longer naps and slowly begin to settle down to a routine that suits both of you, wanting to feed about every three to four hours, on average.

Are you sitting comfortably? Make sure that you find a position that is comfortable for the two of you. There's nothing worse than trying to feed your baby whilst you are horribly aware of the fact that your left leg has gone completely numb and is about to drop off. Often putting a pillow under the baby to raise her up a little helps, and so does putting your feet up.

Breast-feeding

Getting started If there's a delay in starting to breast-feed, your baby may refuse the breast, especially if longer than forty-eight hours has passed since the birth. Most hospitals will do everything they can to help you establish breast-feeding, so that by the time you go home you and your baby are happy.

At first you will have to help your baby find the nipple. To encourage her natural 'rooting' reflex, gently stroke her cheek; she will turn her head to your breast as you cuddle her close to you, and cleverly open her mouth. After a couple of days she'll have learnt to do this automatically. Make sure that you are getting the nipple right into the baby's mouth. Unless you do she won't get the milk out easily, and you will get sore nipples.

During the first five minutes your baby will manage to stuff down about 80 per cent of her feed. Usually you won't have to keep her longer than around ten minutes on each breast. Sometimes you'll be able to see she's lost interest – she'll play with your breast or just fall asleep! Don't worry about over-feeding – it's almost impossible with a breast-fed baby.

Don't pull the baby off, ever. Gently loosen her mouth by pressing her chin, or put your finger very gently in the corner of her mouth to loosen the air-lock on your bosom. Pulling her will hurt you.

Keeping up the flow A breast-feeding mother should avoid alcohol, onions, spicy foods and prunes, as all of these go into the milk! She should drink plenty of liquids and get enough rest. Many women find they have excess milk – the best way to maintain a really good milk supply is to empty each breast at each feed. You might consider expressing any excess milk with a small pump (available from most chemists). I have to mention here that breast pumps are the most dreadful things I've ever come across, although other mothers may have wild success with them. Expressing milk is one of the few things I would advise a new mother to do in private, as the sight of her working away at what looks like a lilo pump attached to her bosom may be too much for her husband to bear. He may find it impossible to maintain his earnest new-father-ready-for-anything expression and dissolve into hysteria.

Take care of your breasts Don't forget this: one of the devils of breast-feeding is getting sore, cracked, painful nipples which will make it a miserable experience for you. Wear a well-fitting maternity bra around the clock, if possible, and rub your nipples regularly with a nipple cream.

Stay calm It's always important to remember that your baby is a real litmus paper of all your emotions, and she will be picking up on your vibrations like Lassie. If you are troubled, unhappy, or generally feeling

121

negative, she will be irritable and difficult. And if you're feeling worried and anxious about breast-feeding itself the chances are she will pick up on this and be fractious and uneasy. Always feed the baby as soon as she's hungry so she's not cross before you even start. Talk quietly to her as you feed her so she feels secure, and try to find somewhere quiet so that neither of you is distracted.

The La Leche League, BM 3424, London WCIV 3XX (071 242 1278). *Association of Breast-feeding Mothers*, 18 Lucas Court, Winchfield Road, London SE26 5TJ (081 778 4769).

Bottle-feeding

What kind of milk? Never give a baby under fourteen months unmodified cow's milk: it is dangerous. There is a wide variety of specially prepared baby milk formula available – if in doubt your health visitor will advise you. These baby formulae are designed to get as close as possible to the nutritional make-up of breast milk, so you can rest assured that you are keeping your baby healthy.

How much? It is very important to follow the instructions on the packet exactly and be extremely accurate with your measurements. Too strong or too weak a mixture can harm your baby. It is not a good idea to keep changing the brand of milk powder, either. If your baby gets thirsty between feeds, have a jug of cooled boiled water ready.

Bottles and hygiene You must sterilise each feeding bottle you use, but I've found this endless task a nightmare, and so will you, if, like me, you are prone to worry. I found myself sterilising the same bottle over and over again because I was convinced I'd spotted some horrible bacteria clinging to it . . . Now I use the new disposable bottles which are heaven for neurotics. Not only can you fling them away and know that the next one is going to be completely bacteria-free, but because they are collapsible the baby takes in less air and therefore suffers less wind.

Dummies

An extra comfort Apart from the fact that a dummy does not look at all attractive it can be invaluable in helping to soothe a baby with colic or one who is not breast-feeding but is a 'sucky' baby who still longs for something in her mouth. The anti-dummy brigade will say that all this sucking will result in buck teeth, deformed jaws, speech impediments and a difficulty in weaning the baby off this delicious habit. Any mother who has tried a dummy on her new baby, however, will tell you of the sudden and blissful silence that reigned over the house when the dummy was stuffed for the first time in the baby's mouth. Thumb-sucking is more likely to push the teeth out of position, and is a much harder habit to discourage.

When my daughter Peaches was six months old, she gave up her dummy for the simple reason that it was keeping her awake at night. Every time her dummy dropped out, she blubbed until somebody put it back in again. And of course, it tended to drop out several times a night, which was a pain.

Sensible use Something to be avoided at all costs is dipping dummies into any sugary substance like jam or honey before you put the dummy in the baby's mouth. This will only cause tooth decay. I always found it a helpful rule to keep dummies for naps and bedtime, otherwise there's a danger that you'll use them as a plug in the mouth all day. This may be a way of keeping your baby quiet but it's also a way of keeping her under-stimulated.

Your Baby's Adorable Wonderful Bottom and How to Care for It

One of the greatest joys of parenthood I've found, and one that few baby books ever mention, is the pleasure of gently nibbling on your baby's bottom. You'll notice immediately you have your baby that she has undoubtedly the *most perfect* rear end in the history of the world, and you will be certain that, was Leonardo still alive today, he would make your baby's bum the centrepiece of the Sistine Chapel.

123

Nappies Changing a nappy can be the cause of a lot of fumbling around and feelings of inadequacy at first – but persevere, you'll soon get the hang of it. There is a wide choice of disposable nappy on the market; few people nowadays want to go to the trouble of endlessly washing towelling nappies. If, in a moment of madness, you've decided to use these, you may discover that the washing powder makes the baby sore. Always change a nappy very frequently so that the baby isn't left lying in a fermenting mess – or a pool of wetness.

Nappy rash Being deeply sensitive things, babies' bottoms are alarmingly prone to all manner of minor but very painful sorenesses and rashes. Plastic pants can encourage nappy rash by trapping the widdle and creating heat.

The best treatment for nappy rash is to wash and dry your baby frequently and apply soothing creams specially designed for the purpose. I have found that homeopathic creams such as Calendula are particularly good. Leave the baby's nappy *off* as much as you can, so that the air can get to her bottom. If none of this works, take her to the doctor, as nappy rash has an alarming tendency to get worse.

The amazing Technicolor world of your baby's nappy Most mothers become bewildered and slightly obsessed by the contents of their baby's nappy, and may even take to talking to their GP in purple prose about the myriad hues of acid trip bowel motions.

Most weeny babies open their bowels several times a day, but less frequently as they get older. Your baby's very first bowel motions will be sticky and greenish black: do not faint – this is called meconium and is normal. If the meconium hasn't appeared within forty-eight hours of birth, you should tell the doctor. After the meconium a little baby will do watery poos which are marginally more comforting to look at. Breast-fed babies poo less often than bottle-fed babies because the milk is more completely absorbed. Don't panic if your breast-fed baby doesn't poo for a couple of days. If she has an unusually large number of dirty nappies it may be that something you've been eating is the cause of it.

A bottle-fed baby is likely to have more regular bowel motions. If you notice her straining horribly to poo, however, it means she's a little constipated. Don't hesitate to mention it to your doctor who may recommend a tiny bit of sugar in her water bottle to get a bit of action going. But, wait for it – sugar will turn her poo runny and green.

If your baby is doing horribly smelly, hard, or *furiously* runny poos, get in touch with the doctor.

Baby, Don't Cry . . .

The sound of a baby's crying has an astonishing effect on mothers – rather like in those spy films, where Russians play a mind-bending noise down the telephone and the recipient falls to the ground, kicking and screaming and confessing everything. A baby's cry can make you absolutely ill and demented trying to find ways to quell her misery. But babies have to cry to express their needs, or they wouldn't survive.

What does she want? As you get to know your baby better and better during these first few weeks together, you'll learn to identify her different cries.

A hunger cry is quite rhythmical and loud. Trust your feelings: even if you've just fed her, have another go.

A pain cry is very sharp and loud, followed by a pause and then more loud screams. The baby may go red in the face. Quickly investigate any obvious causes and then provide essential comfort by cuddling, singing to or massaging your baby. Some women report success with baby-soothing tapes.

Your baby will have her own tired cry – her eyelids will start to look droopy and she's likely to have a distinctive signal, too. Peaches always rubs her ear, for instance.

An illness cry sounds very whiny, and your baby may be hot and flustered. You will find that nothing soothes for long. *Always* call the doctor if you think she's ill.

Sometimes a baby's cry can simply mean she's bored, lonely, or just wants a cuddle.

At all costs, even when you're feeling thoroughly exhausted, bear in mind that this is *your* baby and *your* instincts will be right. Put your feelings of guilt behind you and try and ignore everybody else's constant tips.

Make sure you hear her cries In a perfect world all little babies would never be far from their mothers while they were sleeping, and we wouldn't need baby alarms. But if your baby is going to be sleeping a distance away from you you must invest in a *good quality* baby alarm. They are vital for any baby sleeping alone in a room: this way she will not be left sobbing hopelessly in the darkness, not knowing where her mother is and becoming more and more inconsolable with every passing second.

When your baby cries too much Sometimes incessant crying can mean your baby has colic, which is a very bad tummy ache that most babies grow out of by the age of three months. There are no cures for colic, but there are certain things you can do to ease the discomfort. Try changing to the less wind-causing disposable bottles, or to the least 'windy' milk powder, Ostermilk. Or you might try herbal drinks such as camomile tea. Finally, simply holding and cuddling your baby is a huge help.

Your baby may be allergic to the modified cow's milk present in milk powder. A soya-based milk formula may be the answer. There are often other symptoms of milk allergy like wheeziness, diarrhoea or skin rash.

Always seek professional advice before you change your baby's diet. This is vitally important.

Survival tactics If you have an older child as well as a tiny baby, the end of the day is very hectic. I found that the mornings were easier and that they were a good time to prepare the evening meal and get everything straightened up so that the afternoons were free for playing with Fifi and beginning a slow unwinding process with Peaches. We have quite a strict routine in our house, which has helped a great deal. From five o'clock onwards, the time is entirely devoted to getting both children happily ready for bed. They have a bath together and play there for quite a while and have a massage.

I started to massage Peaches, with her sister at her side, as soon as we all got back from the hospital. The first few days I felt a bit sheepish, rather like I ought to wear love beads and a wimple while I was doing it, and I dreaded being caught by our health visitor.

Then one day she came in the early evening: the lamps in the sitting-room were draped with Fifi's red woolly tights, the fire burned merrily, and my girls lay naked on their sheepskins in the middle of the room while I rubbed at them.

'Ah-h-h-h,' said Janet the health visitor, meditatively gazing at the scene.

There was a long pause.

'I'm doing a degree in massage,' she told me, peering into the semi-darkness as a joss stick wafted into her face.

There was another long pause as I kneaded Peaches' fat buttock.

'But my course is on how to massage a baby's aura.'

So, as you can see, you've really never any need to worry about people thinking you're weird . . .

You may feel you're the only mother in the world with a baby who won't stop crying. Friends are extremely important, and you shouldn't allow yourself to become too isolated. It may seem a mortifying idea, but try chatting to the mothers you meet in the clinic, the park, the swimming pool, even the shopping queue. Obviously I'm not suggesting that these contacts should form the entire basis of your social life, but certainly at the beginning having a supportive friendship with another woman who's in the same boat can be a great help when you're feeling at your wits' end.

If you feel desperate you can phone the support group for parents with babies who cry all the time: *Cry-sis* 071 404 5011.
Also available from *Cry-sis*, the excellent *Crying Baby – How to Cope* by Pat Grey (Wisebuy Publications).

The Untold Advantages Of the Family Bed

Sleeping with your new baby may be something that you feel instinctively is both right for your baby, and very right for you. Parents who decide to share their bed with the baby cease to have a battle at bedtime, or get up in the middle of the night to wander, nightie flapping in a force nine draught, owls hooting in the distance, and baby sobbing inconsolably for comfort, food or something else you can't quite put your finger on. Most new babies do not have a regular sleep pattern and it is no use trying to force one on a tiny baby. She will fall asleep happily in your arms after a feed, and it is silly to believe people who tell you that holding and cuddling your baby to sleep is 'another rod for your back'. Some mothers, myself included, feed their baby in their bed, and have a long cuddling time until the baby is fast asleep, trot off to watch telly with the baby alarm on full blast like feedback at a Grateful Dead concert, and then get in with baby later on.

If you find your baby cries at the mere sight of her cot you have to think that this is probably because already she is associating it with your absence and feeling alone and bewildered, and this is the problem you're dealing with. Never leave your baby to cry herself to sleep as this is really cruel and mean. Imagine if you had a row with your husband, stomped off to the spare room to make your point felt, and he left you there crying all night. Now magnify that a million times to imagine how a new baby feels to be already fighting with the number one person in her life: YOU.

Will we all fit in? Parents who have decided to take the plunge will initially not have to do anything in the way of extending their beds – although once baby starts to get bigger it's wise to consider using the money you've saved on cots, carry cots and prams to put a single bed pushed against your double for extra room for everyone to stretch their legs a bit. Tie the legs of the two beds together and put a blanket over the crack and you won't notice the difference except that you'll have more space. And don't worry about suffocating your baby or rolling over on to her. For some reason, you just don't, it's almost as if parents have a sixth sense that someone small is in bed with them. The only times when you SHOULDN'T sleep with your baby are when you are drugged, drunk, very ill, vastly fat, on a very soft bed like a water bed, or when the baby is tightly swaddled up – but that's all just common sense.

How long for? You may worry how long this arrangement will have to continue, especially if your partner is slightly less enamoured with the idea of the baby's fragrant behind being shoved in his face in the rosy glow of your new nightlight. Babies who have been in their parents' bed for the first year of their lives feel very secure and confident about bedtime matters. They don't associate bed with fuss or trauma, so you'll probably find that your baby starts to drift across the bed to her own space quite naturally, anyway, and in turn into a little bed of her own. If it is you who wishes to change the arrangement you'll need to do it all gently, although if there is an older brother or sister in the family the baby will probably rather happily want to move to their room to share. Our new baby will sleep with us and then we plan for her to move in next door with her slightly larger sister Peaches in a delicious double bed.

Sex You might fear that you won't be able to make a huge noise like a bull winkle shouting over the vast chasms of the tundra, that is, if you're ever able to make love again. Many parents imagine that the baby will wake up and then display cards with scores on them at the end of the steamy session. There are actually a number of solutions to this – the first is to have sex in other, more exotic places; the second is to realise that a happy baby, once she is fast asleep in her cosy shared bed, is often dead to the world and its noise; thirdly, if your baby is a light sleeper who opens an eye at the merest twitch of a groin, put her in a travel cot beside the bed as you work your way through the *Kama Sutra*.

Handling Your Baby

Holding her The first time I ever held Fifi, we just fitted together – luckily for both of us. But many mothers and a lot of fathers find this an anxious moment. A new baby looks so small and breakable: it can be quite frightening working out how to hold her comfortably.

When picking her up, slide one hand under her neck to support her and firmly place the other hand around the upper part of her body. When she's awake, and you're out and about, she'll want the stimulation of looking around, so carry her in an upright position in front of you. Feeling you close behind her will give her extra confidence when meeting new people.

All tiny babies enjoy looking over their mother's shoulder. This position is also good when bringing up wind. But always support her very wobbly head.

She will like being carried around nestled in your arm. To prevent her from slipping, hold her feet with one hand and support her bottom with the other. Until she can hold her head up herself, don't try to pull her up by her arms, as it will yank her head backwards and make her yowl.

Putting her down For the first few weeks, a baby can't move on her own, so she stays in whatever position you put her in. But be careful – some babies become mobile as early as four weeks, and can roll themselves off the bed, like Fifi did. When I had recovered from my cardiac arrest, I ran frantically into the street clutching her to me, and raced to the nearest hospital. The doctor gazed at Fifi, then said to me, 'The only thing wrong with her is she's got too much jewellery on.'

Keeping her close to your heart Physical contact is absolutely essential for all babies. A gentle rocking movement has a soothing effect, and it has been proved that babies who are carried around for much of the time cry considerably less than those who are not. In many societies it is normal for a mother to carry her baby as she does other things, and the slings and papooses now available simply make this pleasurable experience a bit easier on the back and hip. Some new slings leave your arms entirely free for getting on with all the jobs you want to do, or, for that matter, don't particularly want to do, like hoovering the stair carpet (one of the most heinous activities known to womankind).

Often mothering magazines regard pregnancy as a time of frenzied list-writing as mothers-to be all over the country work out how many hundreds of pounds they will spend on 'things' supposedly indispens-able for their new baby. Without wishing to encourage a lynch mob from Mothercare I'd like to say here and now, almost three children later, from my deeply personal researches into this matter, that all a mother needs is a lot of nappies, a pile of babygrows, a large double bed, a little nightlight so she can see at night, and *a pair of strong arms to carry her baby in*. And if she does feel the cheque card flexing in her pocket, she should invest in one of the newest kind of baby slings which can even hold a two year old in comfort in many different positions. I can recommend this kind, having carried a quite fat one year old all day at Disneyland in boiling heat without getting a hernia.

Bathtime Washing a newborn baby can be rather a daunting prospect. I was always terrified that my babies wouldn't be warm enough, and I would start growing yellow feathers all over my bottom and clucking like an old hen as I cranked up the central heating to furnace-like levels, leaving the rest of the family to watch *Panorama* naked downstairs.

My solution to the problem of holding a slippery tiny baby in the water is simply to get into the bath with her, whether you need to wash or not. You could almost certainly do with a few pleasant moments in warm scented (not extremely hot) water with your baby, cuddling and soaping her, and just relaxing. Bathing together will save you craning over the side of the bath, and your baby will be more secure.

A Smaller Splash

Some experts balk at the idea of taking young babies swimming, but I started both of mine very early on. Some mothers, however, do prefer to wait until the baby has had her first injections, because of the risk of infection, but at four weeks both of mine took the plunge with such aplomb that it has been a three-times-a-week thrill for all of us ever since.

The first time I ever took Fifi was at the end of April at the local pool at our home in Kent. When we got there, I discovered that it was an outdoor pool, and that there was frost hanging off the end of our towel. We both got into the baby pool, which was about two feet deep and about four below zero. My husband stood on the edge in a fun-fur-trimmed parka – a non-swimmer managing to look exactly like one of those rabid Olympic trainers who force ten-year-old girls to swim fifty miles before their Ready-Brek. 'Keep swimming, you buggers,' he shouted at us. Fifi and I splashed wanly for approximately two minutes before leaping out of the pool again, possibly never to return.

Despite this tearful and tentative beginning, Fifi did – by the age of nine months – become an accomplished swimmer and diver, and her young sister is now following in her (webbed) footsteps. Not only is swimming marvellous exercise, greatly relaxing and hugely exhausting (resulting in a good night's sleep for all involved), but it's never too soon to conquer the fear of water. You can be less worried around ponds or the sea, knowing that your child can at least stay afloat.

Get her used to the water first Do this in your shared bath at home. It's also a good idea to start having slightly cooler baths from now on, just to get the baby accustomed to water being less than soup temperature. Play splashing and paddling games, and also make sure that she gets used to swishing backwards and forwards through the water with you holding her firmly. This way, she won't mind the odd splash of water on her head and face, and will realise that it's not frightening. Hold your baby firmly under her arms when she's on her back, with one hand under her arms and the other under her head, and under her chest and chin when she's on her front.

Choosing the right pool Find out if there is one of the new-style leisure centres near to you; these often organise mother and baby swimming groups. And if you prefer to go alone, another plus is that the water is considerably warmer than in the old-style pools. Many of the newer pools have what's called a beach-style shallow end, which slopes very gradually down into deeper water and is therefore much safer.

What to take with you Before going, pack your bag carefully. Remember to take a warm change of dry clothes, nappy, bottle, drink of water, a small snack (for the older baby), as swimming is notorious for making even babies ravenous, and two large towels. Some pools do not have changing mats or tables for dressing and undressing a baby. If this is so, take a spare towel to lie your baby on, as the floor will be wet and cold and possibly germy. Don't forget a pair of very small water wings for the baby, as these will make both of you feel secure.

Wise precautions Dress babies who are not potty-trained in a pair of close-fitting plastic pants to prevent unfortunate sewage spills. If you are taking your toddler swimming as well, make sure she goes to the loo, blows her nose and doesn't run on the slippery floors, and remember, never take your eye off her in the water. Don't take a child swimming if she has anything wrong with her or seems to be sickening for anything. The first time you go swimming, you should only stay in about ten minutes, as this is roughly enough for a small baby. The temperature should be at least 85 degrees Fahrenheit (29 degrees Centigrade) in the water for her to be comfortable, and the air should be one or two degrees more than that. Gradually, as you go more and more, you will be able to increase your time in the water.

In the water At first your only aim is getting your baby used to the feeling of being submerged – and by this, I don't mean totally – in water. Mothers worry that even a ducking is going to drown their baby, but in fact a baby's reflex, when dipping under water, is to stop breathing – a legacy of their time in the womb, when they didn't breathe through mouth or nose. Having said this, your aim is not to encourage your child to duck under water as it can still be a shock. Your aim is to promote confidence so that the baby feels safe to enjoy herself.

While playing in the water, always try to keep your face level with your baby's and maintain constant eye contact, as this will give her a safe feeling. Hold her close to you and then bounce very gently up and down. As she gets more used to it, you can hold her away from you, and again, do gentle bouncing and move her backwards and forwards through the water holding her under her arms. As both of you become wild daredevils, you might even try laying her on her back, supporting her with one hand under her hips and the other under the back of her neck. When you have your baby on her front, with one hand under her chest and the other under her hips, you will be amazed to see that she will already try to do arm-and-leg kicking movements. Eventually, you should be able to tow her along by the hands while she's wearing her water wings, as you encourage her to kick.

During all this time, simply by being in the water and playing all these games, your baby will get more and more used to having water on her face. Taking a ball along to the swimming pool also helps, as while playing ball games she will inevitably get splashed a bit. One thing that mothers should remember is that babies tend to forget what they've learned unless they go swimming regularly. It's better to have many, many short but frequent visits to the pool than one long one once a month, which is pretty useless. If you are taking an older child swimming, you can play other games, opening your eyes under water and mouthing 'boo' at each other. The depths you will sink to in order to keep your child amused will, I find, never cease to amaze you. You will wonder why talking about frocks and boys ever used to interest you at all.

When you sense that your baby has become very confident, and you are playing your 'towing along' game, you can start to let go for a few seconds. Then start to encourage her to move through the water by kicking and doggy-paddling. At first, she will seem to swim upright, with no particular stroke at all. As she gets more adept in the water, she will use a more horizontal position and you can start to teach her to push off from the side.

She will grow into a child who is completely at home in the water, and there will be no end to the games that you can play, including jumping in from the side of the pool (with you there to catch), diving between your legs, and both of you diving under the water and coming up holding hands. Pretty soon you will be ready for the synchronised swimming event at the Olympics.

Let Dad Get to Know the Baby

Don't only give the baby to Dad when she is howling her head off and you're sick of her; let him play when the baby's being adorable as well, otherwise you'll create a bad impression of the new addition's personality.

Don't stand around making jokes about how clumsy and useless he is at making bottles, winding baby or changing nappies. Be thankful he's not like my husband who didn't see the baby's bottom until she was about two.

When your husband's been out at work, always remember to fill him in on all the things you and baby have done – new babies are an endless source of anecdotes.

Try hard not to ignore him as you lie in the corner of the sofa canoodling with baby to the complete exclusion of every other life-form in existence. Let Dad join in the cuddling: a father has to fall in love with his new baby, too. It's up to you to smooth the way for him.

The Green-eyed Monster

If this is not your first baby, you may have rosy visions of your children frolicking happily together like a scene out of *The Waltons*. In some cases, after the first few months settling in together, this will come to happy fruition. But in others, the scenario may resemble *Rambo III*. Children who have been only children up until the birth of their new brother or sister often find themselves frightened by the intensity of their anti-baby emotions, and the settling-in process can be a traumatic one. The most important thing, at all times, is to make your older child feel as secure and wanted as she was before.

Sometimes, in spite of all your good efforts, there are children who will take a step back towards babyhood with the arrival of a new baby. These children try to grab your attention by reverting to thumb-sucking, refusing to eat and even bed-wetting. This is not the time for angry, heart-rending scenes but the time for consolation, kisses and reassurance.

The trouble can really start once the new baby is at home, because the older child realises that the baby is here to stay. But you can do much to make her feel extra special. Remember that she will enjoy the fact that age has its privileges – maybe a later bedtime, or an afternoon together to go swimming or to a film, or just out shopping or to the park alone. This will make the older child feel important – although it is also essential not to make her feel too grown-up. Many children resent being constantly told they are a big girl or a big boy now, when inside – despite their bravado – they still feel like your baby.

At all costs, avoid banishing her when you are doing something alone with the baby. Don't send her to her room to play, or to sit in front of the TV alone; let her be involved in whatever's going on, or continue with her own activities with you and the baby near by. You may find that, if you are breast-feeding, she would like to have a go as well. Once will probably be enough, when she discovers it isn't Coca-Cola in one bosom and chocolate milkshake in the other.

If your child does try and deliberately hurt the new baby – which does sometimes happen – remember that, however angry you might feel, she's probably twice as upset by what she's done. You must make it clear that this is not acceptable behaviour, but for a while protect your first-born child from her uncontrollable emotions by not leaving her and the baby alone together until everything has calmed down once again.

Visitors should be reminded in advance *not to ignore* older siblings under any circumstances. I was shocked to discover how many people did this to Fifi when Peaches was born.

The Exploring Parenthood Helpline (071 607 9647).

LOOKING AFTER YOURSELF

Making the Most of the Little Time You Have

1. Pin up a list of the jobs you want to do.
2. Have a nap or a steaming bath when the baby has a nap.
3. Try and tidy up each room as you leave it so that the entire house isn't a chaotic mess by five o'clock.
4. Always let anyone help who offers to do anything!
5. If you are bottle-feeding, make all the bottles for the day in one batch first thing and then store them in the fridge.
6. Make a jelly, so that there's something that vaguely resembles a dessert in the house.
7. Start using disposable bottles. For a teeny bit more expense you'll save hours of time scrubbing away at teats and sterilising bottles.
8. Make easy-to-prepare meals, not ones that need hours of fiddling, cutting peas into the shape of the Arc de Triomphe. Anything that stays quietly in the oven for up to three hours is your friend.
9. Stock up your freezer if you have one.
10. Try to make one comprehensive shopping list and do all the week's shopping on one morning. I always do mine on Monday, and it saves endless toing and froing from the shops. Instead, use that time to go and lie in the park or in your garden with your children.
11. Whenever you are in the country pick vast amounts of roadside flowers. Start cultivating some flowery pot plants, like the very hard to kill Busy Lizzy, around your windows and on tables. Flowers always make a home look delicious, and distract the eye from the dirty laundry pile lurking behind the bedhead.
12. Buy scented candles at the supermarket to create an atmosphere of calm and romance for all of the family.

The Yates Defrost School of Cooking for Guests

Although I take a firm stand against all those jars of baby food, which I really think should only be used in time of dire emergency – the same doesn't always need to apply to one's dealings with adults. Children should not be given chilled foods because of the newly discovered risks of listeria, but it's a different matter when it comes to boyfriends and husbands who return home from work expecting you to be wearing a frilly pair of bri-nylon baby dolls, bending over the hostess trolley, preparing a delicious dinner for six of his business associates. Once you've got a baby in the house, it certainly is useful to know any sneaky ways of cutting corners and giving yourself more time on the sofa with *Young Doctors* and a box of Walnut Whips before the baby cries again.

Until I had Fifi I found it almost impossible to cook, even for myself, let alone guests, without emerging from the kitchen looking like a triffid. Dinner parties were unmitigated disasters with me – far from queening it à la soirée, I was just a puce-faced shadow of the woman I'd been when I entered the kitchen. But then I realised that the secret of successful dinner party cooking was to stay as far away from the kitchen as possible. Using frozen foods and becoming an accomplished fibber was guaranteed to convince everyone I was in fact a direct descendant of Escoffier.

Bin liners Before serving up your chosen meal you must first remove all signs of evidence from sight. Nothing worse could happen to the cheating cook than being caught scraping the last of the *coq au vin* into the casserole dish while a teetering mountain of tin foil wrappers saying 'Feeds two, bake for twenty minutes' lies abandoned near by. Stuff all of this into the bin bag and forget it ever happened.

Camp it up It's also wise for the harassed cook with one ear on her baby to create the impression of a temperamental artiste at work: 'I cannot cook if there are others in the kitchen,' is the best line of defence.

Mushrooms Your greatest ally. The mushroom should be treated with due respect and reverence. It always lends that certain homemade something to anything you are cooking. Throw a lot of mushrooms into a pan and wait until they start to look like mushy snails. Then turf them out over everything except the dessert. Mushrooms look so

repulsive that people always imagine the food is really home-cooked, and couldn't possibly be mistaken for frozen food which is prepared to look vaguely aesthetically pleasing.

Where to buy Marks and Spencer's is of course the heaven of the frozen food aficionado; their shepherd's pie is almost indistinguishable from the real thing, once you've hit it a couple of times to take the pattern of the Bayeux Tapestry off the mashed potato on top. Many men measure your devotion by the amount of potatoes you are willing to peel. Actually, the only time I've ever fainted was when I was bending over our flip-top bin looking for the potato scraper which I'd dropped into half a ton of peelings.

Casserole dishes These are an excellent buy because obviously dinner will look better in one of these than flopping on to the plate in a plastic bag. Let stew loosen up to fit the shape of the dish first and disguise gaps with grated cheese.

Foreign terminology References to Nooovelle Cweezeen come in useful if your vegetables are half cooked, and there aren't enough of them to go round. *Al dente* should apply to anything which seems to be still frozen in the middle. An ordinary bacon sandwich can transmogrify into *porc au pain* – pain being the operative word after you've got it off the kitchen floor from the scalding-hot grill.

When they want to know more If there are mad people at the table who ask you to write out a recipe, just smile sweetly and say it's a family secret passed down through generations . . .

The Baby Blues

Many things can trigger post-natal depression, although it is best to regard it as merely one's hormones getting back to normal, and in the meantime creating a tumult of passions and miseries. Exhaustion doesn't help, and your feelings of not being able to cope may be increased by now having realised how dependent a new baby really is. Post-natal depression affects 50–75 per cent of mothers about the fourth day after giving birth. It's a mild reaction lasting a day or two in most cases, but sometimes it can turn into a clinical depression which is an illness. This affects one in ten mothers. These women are devastated after their high hopes of happiness with their new baby are not fulfilled. There are also cases of post-natal psychosis, which is far rarer – affecting only about one in five hundred women. This takes the form of a truly acute breakdown, sometimes with schizophrenic reactions involving delusions or hallucinations.

Try not to take on too much; don't begin any demanding projects; avoid hot, overcrowded places and don't panic if everything seems to have come to a bit of a standstill. Also, it's wise to remember that you don't have to feel guilty about seeming to be snowed under, or having manic mood swings. This is a combination of fluctuating hormones and almost no sleep. It's a good idea, if you can, to nap while the baby naps and not to feel you have to use this time to do the laundry. Stuff the laundry.

The Association for Post-Natal Illness gets between a hundred and five hundred letters and phonecalls every week from mothers who are convinced that they are slowly going mad and will never recover. The Association stresses that mothers feeling such misery must seek immediate medical help and change doctors if they have one who is dismissive or unsympathetic to their plight. It is comforting to realise that there is in fact a 100 per cent recovery rate, although it can be a slow process. Mothers who have suffered from post-natal depression suggest the following self-help list:

Accept help from your doctor or health visitor If you can't make it to the surgery, ring up and ask for a home visitor.

Talk Once you've sought out professional help, make it clear what your feelings and anxieties are. You may find some friends are unsympathetic and think you should just 'pull yourself together'. The National Childbirth Trust is likely to be a good source of one-to-one counselling.

Eat properly It's important, while feeling depressed, not to starve yourself. A drop in your blood sugar may bring on a panic attack or a fit of crying, so always keep a small bar of chocolate or a muesli bar handy. Avoid alcohol and caffeine of any kind, and check with your doctor just in case he discovers you're anaemic. After pregnancy, many women find that they are especially lacking in iron and zinc (that's why your hair may thin, too).

Have time for yourself One of the things that can make a woman feel depressed is rather a frivolous one. It is the feeling that, with a new baby in the house, there is never a second to do any of the languid, pleasurable, purely personal and pampering activities she enjoyed before. Suddenly, you have turned into a woman who can't shave her legs in the bath, because the baby's in with you and she'll drown if you let go; can't find time to make a hair appointment and has greasy hair and three inches of root showing. None of your clothes fit and you don't want to buy any new ones, in case you get lazy about getting your shape back. I think the factor of feeling like a blancmange may be underestimated by doctors when it comes to post-natal depression. It is a horrible feeling to wake up every morning more exhausted than when you went to bed and gaze at a vast expanse of wobbling white flesh that wasn't there before. The answer here, though, is not to compound the problem by comfort eating, but indulge in 'comfort swimming'!

Make sure that your husband keeps his ear open for the baby after she has gone to bed, and give yourself an hour every evening to lock yourself in the bathroom with a magazine and some bubble bath. Or try and arrange with another mum to have her baby for one afternoon a week, while she has yours for a different afternoon. You can use this time to go out *on your own* to an adult education class, a trip to the hairdresser, or a visit to a friend to catch up on gossip.

Learn to say no Refuse anything that you know will cause you extra work and stress, such as going to a party if you don't feel up to it, or playing hostess to endless visitors. When you are in a situation that can't be wriggled out of, learn to delegate. Surprisingly, people never mind lending a hand when asked, but when not asked they think you don't need it.

Try to go out every day Sitting in a darkened room in a crumpled heap on the bed, sobbing along to Leonard Cohen (or even George Michael) is to be avoided at all costs. Or have a friend round, someone you don't have to put on airs and graces for and can be yourself with.

Learn to relax and think positively Maybe now is the time to learn yoga or meditation, if you have managed to arrange your one afternoon a week off. You can then maintain your new-found knowledge at home. Some local swimming pools also do massages, which may rid you of many knots and tensions, especially if combined with a sauna or Turkish bath. Remember that this is a temporary phase, and thousands of other mothers feel the same way. It's not your fault that you are ill, and like all other illnesses, this will pass and you will get better.

Don't get pregnant again too soon It's important not to start another baby until you are fully better. If you have very severe post-natal depression, you may need drug treatment, for example, that can't be given in early pregnancy. You may also find that the Pill causes further depression, however, so talk to your GP about alternative forms of contraception available.

Pre-menstrual tension Doctors have found there is a link between pre-menstrual tension and post-natal depression. If your menstrual cycle has restarted, it's a good idea to keep a chart. If there is a definite monthly pattern, you may be able to get hormone therapy. One self-help remedy is to take Evening Primrose oil capsules, and Vitamin B6. Acupuncture has also been known to work wonders.

The Association for Post-Natal Illness, 7 Gowan Avenue, London SW6 6RH (071 731 4867).
Meet-A-Mum Association, 5 Westbury Gardens, Luton, Beds LU2 7DW (0582 422253).

Getting Back Into Shape Gently

After the baby is born, visitors often bring not only floral tributes, but also chocolates. I must be one of the few people to put on half a stone after they've given birth, because of the mammoth amount of truffles I managed to consume. The day afterwards, I went to have my bath and couldn't find the plug beneath my fat, I was still so porky. I moved faster than any woman who has just had a baby has ever moved, and dragged the weighing scales out of the bathroom next door. When I got on them my heart sank. I'd rather expected to have lost a stone, not had a 7½lb (3.4kg) baby and put on weight.

I stood on one foot to see if that made a difference. Then I took off my earrings and the sticking plaster on my arm to see if either were contributing to this worrying plateau stage. Then, as there was wisely no full-length mirror on the maternity ward, I balanced precariously on the side of the bath and peered into the two-inch square mirror, thoughtfully provided about ten feet up the wall. The two inches I could see looked rather attractive, I decided. It was a pity the rest of me looked like something you forced your best friend to eat for you at school dinners. My thighs looked exactly like a dessert we used to call 'Dingle Froth'. I went back to my room and finished off the truffles. 'Tomorrow is another day,' I said dramatically to a baffled Fifi.

The question is, do women really need to put on 28lb (12kg)? Absolutely, say doctors. The weight you should have put on will not all have been on your stomach. More than half the gain is in fluid and fat stores and increased blood volume, which is distributed all over the body. Your silhouette will have broadened in all the places women broaden: hips, thighs, bottom, upper arms. And the extra fluid your body will have been carrying around will probably have gone to your legs and feet, making them feel very heavy and swollen.

When to start Some doctors don't like women to start exercising immediately, but others advise them simply to follow their instincts and start doing some gentle exercises as soon as they like. I followed my instincts – into the kitchen, mainly. Also, making a routine for exercise seemed much more difficult. But when I did start, two weeks later, I did exercises with Peaches near by, and quite a lot of them with her actually on top of me. You may like to do it all to music, and the baby will love that.

Get ready Before doing any exercise, go through a series of stretches to get warmed up, otherwise injuries can occur. You can't expect your body to snap back into shape immediately. And don't strain your back before you've started by lifting the baby incorrectly: bend at the knees and use your legs, rather than bending over at the waist.

If you're stll breast-feeding, try to feed your baby before you start, so that your breasts are less heavy. And always wear a good, supportive sports bra, it's your greatest investment.

Work at post-pregnancy pace: your heart has been beating for two for nine months and will continue to do so for a few weeks after the delivery. Slow down your old exercise pace to avoid getting dizzy.

Stretch those limbs The stretches I learned were simple and easy to remember. Start by rolling your head around twenty times in each direction to relax the neck, then make wide, circular movements with your shoulders, ten in each direction, with both shoulders moving simultaneously. Put one leg up on to a work surface, in the kitchen, for example; stretch your arms up and then slowly bring them down on to the outstretched leg, reaching round the ankle. Then slowly lower your body down on to the leg as far as you can stretch out. Repeat ten times, if you can, and then change to the other leg.

If you have someone around to help you, try this next. Lie on your back with one leg stretched up into the air. Ask someone to stand in front of you and gently press the leg back towards your body; feel the thigh muscles stretching out, count to ten, and release. Repeat on the other leg.

Stand up, with your legs as far apart as you can manage, toes pointing ahead. Stretch your arms into the air, then lower them to one side stretched out. Look ahead of you, not down at the floor; stretch back up into the air and repeat the other side. Then stretch up again from the same position. Slowly reach down to clasp ankle with both hands, one around the front and one around the back. Repeat on the other leg.

Again, stretch upwards and clasp one hand on each forearm and bend from the waist, letting your arms swing freely down as near to the floor as you can manage.

Do not strain to reach any of these; don't hurt yourself; do as much or as little as you can manage. You'll find that each time you attempt the stretches, you get better and it gets easier.

Your tummy Roll-ups are a gentler form of sit-up. Lie on the floor with your hands clasped behind your neck and gently roll up towards your knees. This tightens the upper abdomen. Try to do it half a dozen times and then start to build up. If you feel rather energised and ready for something with a bit more attack to it, I suggest you attempt these torturous around-the-home exercises:

Your bottom and legs Step-ups are a fantastic, truly effective exercise which will almost kill you the first few times. Well, they almost killed me. Simply place a low stool – it should be 12–18in high – in front of you and then stand up on it. Repeat this ten times using first your left leg to get on the stool and then down again and then the other leg. Build your repetitions as you get stronger. If you feel really ambitious, you could try holding something heavy in each hand while you step up and down.

Your posture Try standing with your back against the wall, holding the baby if you wish. Then, walking your feet out a little bit, bend your knees and sit in an imaginary chair. Your thighs will carry your weight and your back should be straight against the wall. Then inhale and push your tummy out; exhale and pull it in. Make your tummy move as much as you can.

When a More Drastic Régime is Called for

Despite doing these gentle exercises after Peaches was born, I couldn't help noticing that skimpy underwear was still out of the question. I'd taken to wearing polo-necked pants, and I would pull these up at high velocity every morning in order to trap my fat bits in the knicker elastic.

I went to Harrods and had to take out a second mortgage in order to buy a special white cream the assistant assured me was going to sandblast my cellulite into oblivion. I hoped that it would also take part of my bottom away with it. Always the great believer in mystical claims, I imagined my bottom being raised to such a height people passing me in the street would mistake it for epaulettes. But after the first session with the gritty cream the bath felt like the inside of a cement mixer and my skin had funny little bits of plaster-cast all over it – but that was the only difference. Finally, in desperation, I decided to employ a trainer. Someone who would shout abuse at me, like the sergeant in *An Officer and a Gentleman*; someone who was willing to take on the challenge of getting me back into a swimsuit in two weeks – and out of the chin-length knickers!

I felt like my body was in shock from the night feeds, and was unprepared for a visit to Sainsbury's, let alone one of those nightmarish gyms where fifteen-year-old sex goddesses in Lycra thong bikinis lift dumb-bells in front of huge mirrors. I didn't yearn for the joys of locker room camaraderie at all. What I wanted to find were exercises I could do at home, with no one watching and the kids near by. What really decided me to get a trainer to introduce me to the joys of running, walking and abdominal exercises were my drawers.

The most athletic thing I managed to do the first day was get out of our house in my red shorts without anyone seeing my thighs. I lurked by the front door, hiding behind convenient bits of furniture. 'God,' muttered the pulsatingly healthy professional, as he chained his racing bike to my railings, 'we'll need a double door to get that backside through.'

And so I was introduced to the first fact about personal trainers: they insult you horribly for two hours a day, and you have to give them money for it. The second thing I learned, that very first morning, is that they have no feelings and show no mercy – even if you cry, which I did.

My trainer explained to me that most of his exercise régime is carried out in the parks around London. Cold air helps burn off some of the excess fat, although, in my case, Battersea would have had to suffer a sudden Ice Age to have any effect. Much of the exercise session is taken up with making people run. Strange as it may seem, I wasn't even sure how to do that properly. How often does anyone actually *run*? And I don't mean that delicate running we all do for buses. The trainer explained to me that jogging around is completely useless. 'You see people doing it all the time in parks. It does them no good at all,' he said. So he made me run half the way to Battersea Park from my house and walk when I thought I was about to die.

When we got there, he led me to a clearing and there, horror of horrors, was a track – a track! And next to it a little hut with a tiny, empty gymnasium in it. I was quite distraught to find that these dreaded facilities lay less than twenty minutes from my front door.

Fast walking and running are invaluable: I was made to run up and down a steep hill. Unfortunately for me, there was a one-in-three mountain near my home, which he made me tackle. This was possibly the most horrible experience of the whole exercise programme, but definitely lifted my bottom, which was the personal trainer's equivalent of raising the Titanic...

After a week with the trainer, I was already stronger, and felt a lot less tired because all the fresh air gave me more energy. The shouting never let up. The trainer also tried to pretend he wasn't with me because my tracksuit was lime-green and belonged to someone half my size. And, because he made me do my training regardless of the weather, I kept wearing Bob's ankle-length anorak and a knitted hat a plumber had left behind years ago.

By the end of week two, I had lost weight and felt even more fit. I was having to combine the running with the Misery Plan diet – no Big Macs (or meat of any kind) and no chocolate. Surprisingly, pasta was OK. Of course by day three I was fantasising about chocolates and had become the sort of girl who gets excited about a sultana.

I began to dream of sharing the podium with Carl Lewis in Barcelona – until one day a road-runner shot past me and my trainer told me it was Christopher Chataway, who'd been running for years. I felt considerably chastened; I decided that maybe Flojo hadn't retired because of me. 'Of course, that's just a jog for him,' added my trainer, running on ahead.

The Fun Starts Here

Starring

Fifi

and

Peaches

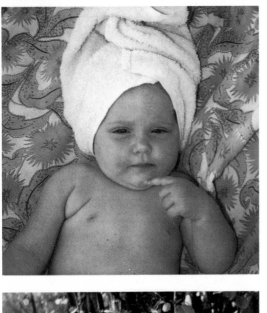

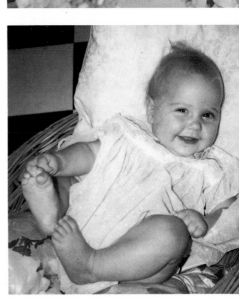

A Word About Diet

Nothing drastic Most new mothers' hearts sink at the thought of having to diet when their energy is so taken up with looking after the baby. I wouldn't therefore recommend a serious diet at this stage – don't ever feel tempted to starve yourself. Most diets make your blood more acidic, which makes you feel stressed – not how you want to feel with a new baby around the house. However, if you exercised for only half an hour a day, you could use up 500–1,000 calories – which would melt away about 1lb (500g) a week. Breast-feeding uses up a massive 600–800 calories a day, which is why it is imperative that you forget about dieting while you're doing it.

If you are not breast-feeding, you might think about a day-long fruit fast, which is excellent for cleaning out the system. By the end of the day I tried it, I felt that if I had any more apple juice I'd grow a stalk; I got an appalling headache, and had to keep pressing my forehead on the kitchen tiles every time I went down for another grape. However, there are real benefits, but never go on a fruit fast for more than two days, and it's a good idea to stick to just one kind of fruit, as this is less of a strain on the digestive system.

The most important thing is simply to start re-training your body not to expect enough food for a family of fifteen. Stop treating yourself to things. Pregnancy may be the one time in a woman's life when she thinks she can get away with it, but once the baby's come all that has to stop (which is sad for those of us who were working our way through the Thornton's catalogue).

How to lose 52lb (23.5kg) in a year It's quite astonishing the amount of weight that you can lose in one year, simply by giving up certain foods that you eat every day without realising their calorie content. For example, if you gave up one teaspoon of cream in your coffee, you would lose 6lb (2.7kg) in one year. If you gave up one doughnut a day, you would lose 25lb (11.3kg) in a year. If you gave up one teaspoon of butter on your toast, you would lose 11lb (5kg) in a year. If you gave up one can of fizzy drink each day, you would lose 17lb (7.7kg) in a year. One tiny, 2oz (56g) chocolate bar would rid you of 18lb (8.1kg) in a year. If you gave up one muesli bar a day, you would lose 25lb (11.3kg). This is a far less painful way of shedding the extra weight you are carrying than going on a rigid diet, although you have

149

to be prepared to lose the weight slowly. But you will benefit from improved energy and well-being and therefore cope better with the onslaught of motherhood.

What Can I Wear Now?

You may not be able to fit back into your old ski pants immediately and you may have already burnt all your maternity dresses, but there are ways of disguising extra curves while you're whittling them away. Think of simple, fluid shapes. Your clothes should enhance you rather than strangle you. Hard as it may be to accept, after months of wearing a Demis Roussos-style marquee, a body-hugging boob tube may not be the ideal garment for you – anyway, it looks pretty stupid over a maternity bra. Knitwear and soft jumpers will be perfect because you will have something to put inside your jumper. Clothes with slightly padded shoulders, however sneered at by the fashion cognoscenti, are great for disguising a fat rear end. If you are going to buy clothes for the in-between stage, get them a little bigger rather than smaller.

A lot of people say that buying something tight will encourage you to lose weight. Actually, it will encourage you to want to shoot yourself. One-colour dressing creates an illusion of slenderness, and everyone will tell you to avoid belts, but I know this is impossible for anyone who's just spent nine months looking portly. All you will have dreamed of is being able to truss yourself up in the middle, even if it does make you look like a bratwurst. Whatever you're wearing, it's a good simple idea to try to stand up properly, although, after I had Peaches, I have to admit the last thing I wanted to do was get out of bed, let alone think about my posture. Slouching does make your stomach and your bottom stick out. You may also discover that you've got into bad posture habits during the last few months.

Finally, try to avoid skirts with vast amounts of fabric at the hip, as it bounces up like a tyre if you're not careful. If you have a pot belly, though, remember it is one bit of a girl which turns many men into savage love beasts.

It's also a good idea not to look at pictures of famous mothers who've just had babies. Remember the photographer has probably trapped all their extra fat in a bulldog clip at the back. While I was expecting, I read an interview with one actress who said she'd had to be smuggled out of the maternity wing so she didn't depress all the other new mothers because she was looking so beautiful. This is just the sort of comment which deserves a punch up the bracket.

What Sex Life?

One of the traumas facing couples after the birth of a new baby is readjusting their sex lives to the new demands of having a family. These problems tend to come for two reasons: the first one could be called 'post-partum loss of plot'. By this I mean that most mothers, and not only first-time mothers, find that they feel distressed at the changes in their bodies and because of this sudden lack of confidence, they also seem to forget how to dress. This is a period when women can become obsessed by their looks and by their clothes.

In turn, husbands may be completely baffled by their wives' sudden obsession with what they see as extremely minor physical flaws, and that's if they've even noticed them. And since many men will also find that they are going through an identity crisis, just because they have become fathers, they may lose patience and much-needed sympathy much quicker. Instead of being supportive about stretch marks, they may be trying to hear how much their wives still find them attractive instead.

During this period, when women tend to feel in the sexual doldrums, finding their new baby all-consuming and exhausting, a man must skip between two completely contradictory roles. Not only does he have to be understanding about his wife's lack of desire, at the same time he must constantly reassure her that he finds her hugely attractive. No one is remembering to tell him he is attractive, and he probably longs for the closeness and reassurance of lovemaking.

While fatherhood does not produce dramatic physical changes equal to those of motherhood, many men do go through a crisis, and start worrying about ageing. Both becoming a mother and becoming a father changes the way we think of ourselves and the way others perceive us, and it is simply a matter of time before both of you will adjust to your new self-image. It's difficult initially to switch your identity from being your baby's mother to being a wild, sizzling lover. But time does rapidly assist in this matter.

The thing to aim at throughout those difficult early months, is not

151

to let habit rule the day. Many couples have found that their lovemaking difficulties arose because they always made love once they went to bed, and of course, as any new mother will tell you, the minute she's in bed, she's unconscious. Sometimes merely changing the routine by either going to bed earlier or making love in different places removes the pressures of the bedroom. Just talking to your partner about how you feel means that neither of you will allow misconceptions to blow up out of all proportion. Keep communication open at all times, and have sex on the kitchen table. And all should be well in six months.

Chapter Five

Days

of

Heaven

By now you'll be used to the upheaval of having a new baby around the house, and you'll probably be feeling a lot better, too – by the second six months of your baby's life you'll have most of your figure back! You'll have more of a routine worked out and be freer to do some things just for yourself – so much more difficult at the beginning when any spare moments you have are spent fast asleep or trying to remember what it was like in the days when getting to water the begonias didn't have to be treated like an operation needing military timing in between naps, feeds, changes and domestic activities.

Don't forget to make time to be with your baby for pleasure. Now you're more in control, you can have those days of heaven with a baby who's more and more fun. You'll become more adventurous in your trips out with her, and realise that your social life doesn't have to come to a halt. Babies are immensely portable, and enormously nosey, too!

One of the things that goes hand in hand with seeing more people is coming into contact with those who hugely underestimate what mothering is about. When you tell them you've got fifteen children all under the age of six they look perplexed and ask what you do all day. These are the people who assume there is no life and no stimulation without a career outside, forgetting cinemas, reading, painting, gardening – all those things you're still able to enjoy. Having said that, there are bound to be things you will miss and indeed perhaps even envy: friends without children who are still trundling to work on a filthy commuter train do have the rewards of enough money to go into Miss Selfridge without hyperventilating with guilt and ending up in a babywear shop. They have whole entire days off uninterrupted by the patter of small feet and the incessant call of 'Mum-eeeeee'. They are not tired on the same gargantuan scale, they have lie-ins, they don't fall asleep on the stairs outside the loo at parties.

You may even find that some friends will be lost – the ones who think you talk about your child all the time and have lost touch with world politics. But you've swopped them for someone far sweeter who will kiss you a lot more!

It has to be said that you may find yourself leaning against the sink shouting at your partner that he doesn't understand, it's all right for him, and voicing that great cry of all mothers at home, 'If you had any idea of how much I do all day you'd drop down dead . . .' You'll know the absolutely relentless quality of looking after a baby day after day, but if you're organised, you won't feel your home's in chaos, and be too tired to experience the bliss of watching your baby becoming more and more accomplished.

That first birthday party will be a momentous occasion, as she sits there, red-faced and beaming, leaning forwards in anticipation of her first bite of birthday cake. You and your partner can exchange a glance of great pride that you have lived through this exhausting and wonderful year.

CARING FOR AN OLDER BABY

Watching Her Change

Three to five months At around three months your baby will be able to hold a rattle briefly, if you place it in her grasp, and also be spending hours gazing at her hands, realising that they're attached to her. Now is the time to provide little toys for your baby to hold, chew and bang. The amount your baby will be sleeping will vary immensely from about ten to twenty hours in every twenty-four. As her spine gets stronger and she begins to uncurl, she will enjoy sitting in one of those bouncing baby chairs watching you doing whatever you are doing. If you don't have a bouncy chair, prop her up on a pile of pillows and cushions so that she can always see what's going on.

In the first months of a baby's life, nature seems to have arranged it so that all the best smiles are kept for mother. Wisely, I feel, as she is the one that has to get up at four in the morning to change nappies. But rapidly, your baby will start to take notice of her dad and brothers and sisters, and soon they will be greeted with grins of recognition and loving coos, which is most gratifying.

By the fourth month, you will find that some babies start to hanker after solid food, although many are still happy on breast or formula milk after six months.

By four months, most mothers can hardly believe that the bouncing, loud, grinning, endlessly sociable, gorgeously pretty baby sitting there is the same little tiny scrap they brought home from hospital. Between four and six months, your baby will start to wave her arms and legs wildly, when placed on the floor on her tummy, in imitation of Mark Spitz. She will already be thinking about crawling, and may even manage to roll herself over in different directions. If there is anything around that is potentially dangerous or pull-offable, remove it from

157

her sight and reach. The first great law of baby behaviour is, if it's pull-offable, they'll pull it off.

Five to eight months Babies of five or six months love to spend time playing with their mothers. This seems like a case of stating the obvious, but you may not realise that your time is the greatest gift you can give your young baby. All the new things that she's learning to do – and you will be astonished at the range of your small baby's abilities – she wants to share with you. At the moment, you will probably find that she spends hours grabbing her feet and eating them. She will also enjoy rolling from her stomach to her back, and then back again, although occasionally a plump baby may find that she's good at rolling in one direction and then gets stuck. Boredom is to be avoided at all costs; babies at this age really need to play Round-And-Round-the-Garden, Peep-bo, This Little Piggy, and will start to enjoy looking at baby books.

Ignore half-finished chores, and get down on the floor and into the exuberant spirit of all these games. As your baby becomes more mobile she will keep wanting to try and stand up, with you holding her, and bounce all over you and pretend to be flying. Remember that nothing is safe if it's within reach, and everything she reaches will go in her mouth. I once gave Fifi my toothbrush to play with, and, when I came back into the room, she was firmly scrubbing and inserting it into our dog's bottom, as he lay by the fire. Neither the dog nor I have ever been the same since, although I was amazed at how dexterous she was at such an early age.

By six months, she will probably have moved into a highchair of her own, and you may also notice that, as she gets more used to being fed with a spoon, she'll want to have a go herself. This is extremely messy, and it's smart to put a bin-bag or newspaper on the floor under the high chair for these first attempts at feeding herself. Another good idea is to put a selection of finger foods, such as chopped up peaches and bananas, green beans and boiled carrot slices, on to her high-chair tray, so she can eat those on her own.

Most babies at this time will be teething. She may be miserable and cry and dribble a lot. You can ease the discomfort of new teeth by putting soothing gel on her gums, and giving her a teething ring to hold and chew on. That first glorious tooth should be accompanied by her first toothbrush. There are special toothpastes for little babies, and now is the time to renew your efforts to avoid all sugary foods and drinks.

At six or seven months she will start making plenty of 'double' sounds when she is talking to you, and perhaps also her first 'da'. Or even 'dada'. Sometimes, a baby who has previously talked a lot stops talking so much, and mothers worry that something is wrong. If your baby is not reacting to sounds that are made behind her, seek advice from your GP or health visitor.

By seven months, many babies will be getting ready to crawl. She will also be able to sit up unaided, even if it's just for a short while.

Nine to twelve months Towards the end of the first year, your baby will make a great effort to pull herself up into a standing position and will be getting ready to start walking. Now is the time to make sure that, if your baby is sleeping in a cot, she hasn't got too far to fall if she makes a valiant attempt at climbing out of it. Having got up, some babies aren't too sure about how to get down again and spend some time working out how to get back down safely. Quickly remove any furniture that's wobbly, put precious or dangerous ornaments in a high place, get rid of your tablecloths and be extra careful with any wires, plugs or pan handles. Your baby will certainly be crawling by now. Some babies prefer crawling along on their bottoms, and some use their arms. But most of them learn to get around the furniture at high speed in a very short time.

From about nine months onwards, a baby's language improves astonishingly. When she speaks, you will hear the nuances and inflections of proper talking. She could even be saying quite a few words if you've been talking to her a lot. You will hear the tone of questions and she will interrupt if you are chatting with your girlfriends. To this day, I am unable to conduct a conversation on the phone or on the sofa with my best friend without Miss Beaky joining in, and it's been like that since she was about four months old.

By a year, your baby will have her own words, which probably only you and close friends of your family will understand, but they will be real words for real things. She will also probably have about three, perfectly recognisable words, and some babies have a lot more than that. If you say the same things frequently to your child, she will soon repeat them.

At about ten months, you will notice the first signs of stroppiness. She will be developing her own sense of will and will show frustration and even anger if it is thwarted. Babies are very easily distracted, and you can avert minor tantrums by providing a fascinating alternative. I found reading on the sofa together a cosy, restful activity and it was at this age that I introduced the hideously messy practice of hand-painting. Now that she is so much better at using her hands, picking up and pulling things along, you can also start to show her the rudiments of drawing, whereas before, she would have simply eaten the paper.

Your baby will probably be drinking from her own little cup and feeding herself as well if you have been letting her practise, however messily, for the last few months. She will also suddenly become rather co-operative, holding out an arm or a leg when you are dressing her. Some babies become rather suspicious of strangers. A baby of this age will wonder at absolutely everything and will gaze with rapt attention at the beauty of the world, reminding you of what you've got used to ignoring.

Yum, Yum: When Your Baby Starts to Eat Proper Food

Weaning Babies have to be weaned eventually because milk alone doesn't provide enough nourishment for them to grow into princesses, executives and lumberjacks – but starting to give your baby solids earlier than recommended will *not* make her grow any better, in fact, having solids before the age of four months can cause bad food allergies. Mothers of bottle-fed babies tend to wean their children before those who breast-feed. It seems right not to be in too much of a hurry to get the baby off the breast, given the nutritional advantages. Probably the best advice about when to wean is to watch your baby and take your lead from her. If she still seems hungry after plenty of feeds then it's time to start to introduce her to solid foods, choosing very carefully what she eats, as good food is a building block for her future health.

At first, try just one food at a time. Baby rice is a good one to start with. This way you can keep an eye open for anything that disagrees with her. Initially your baby will only eat a weeny bit of food. Don't ever let mealtimes become a battleground by forcing the baby to eat something she doesn't want; be calm and relaxed about it. Even little babies enjoy the social aspect of eating: chatting with you, experimenting with the food, spoon, cup, bottle, and watching other members of the family.

What should she eat? Recently, because of the scares associated with tins and jars of baby food, many mothers have been re-thinking the way they feed their children, having never considered feeding their children homemade food. It has to be said that this is mad: specially prepared baby foods are not some miracle concoction. This is a myth that has been promoted by the makers. Manufactured baby foods are not even particularly time-saving. It is as quick, and much, much cheaper, to feed your child with whatever the rest of the family is eating, all zooshed up in a blender or food processor.

Obviously, there are a few guidelines that need to be followed. Remember that babies under fourteen months should not be given unmodified cow's milk. There should be no salt in any of your baby's meals, and you mustn't add salt to the water in which you cook the vegetables. Babies' bodies cannot cope with salt and it can be dangerous. Beware the hidden salts in foods like salami, bacon, tinned ham and corned beef. Avoid sugar as much as possible: here again there are many hidden dangers: baked beans, for example, are high in sugar unless you buy special brands. For general safety, avoid small hard things like peanuts until a baby is at least four years old. Once your baby is over six months and can start to have food that isn't always puréed, make sure the bits of food you give her aren't small enough to choke on or to get stuck in the throat. I remember taking Fifi to a Duran Duran concert when she was two, and she stuck a peanut into her nostril during the encore. Egg yolk is suitable for babies once they are six months old, but they shouldn't have egg white until they are nine months old, and then you must ensure the egg is very well cooked.

Both breast-fed and bottle-fed babies benefit from vitamin supplements, which are usually given in drops. I have used these from the age of six months up until five years.

Maybe you are planning to bring your baby up to be vegetarian. Take care to ensure she is being properly nourished and receiving all the vitamins that she needs. At five to six months, she will be ready to try puréed lentils with vegetables and stewed fruit, and then at teatime mashed banana or other soft fruits, as well as her usual milk feed. At six to eight months you will be able to start her on soaked, dried fruits, tofu, cottage cheeses, eggs and nut creams.

Cooking for your baby I am a great advocate of any kind of casserole, be it vegetable- or meat-based, which can be stuffed into the oven on a low light and left to simmer gently all day so that a delicious filling hot meal can be given to everyone in the evening without a horrible rush. I bought two small pudding-sized steamers, so that I could quickly make all kinds of hugely fattening, madly popular steamed puddings for desserts on the days when everyone wanted a change from fresh fruit. They are marvellously comforting and homely, take no time to steam away for a couple of hours undisturbed by any human contact, and emerge golden and triumphant at the dinner table.

Fish and chicken pieces are quick to cook and go down very well with a little mashed potato and vegetables. I steam our vegetables until they are really soft and mash them for the baby. Babies enjoy a small dish of mixed vegetables topped with grated cheese, with a yoghurt to finish, or a banana, or a little sandwich, with ham or salady stuff in it. Any pasta dishes, with cheese or meat sauces go down well – and if you're really stuck, use potato as your base and mix in with your mini blender anything of the following: carrots, parsnips, broccoli, broad or runner beans, cauliflower florettes, or even courgettes.

Be scrupulous with general kitchen hygiene and thoroughly wash all utensils. I always boil the bowl, spoon and hand blender once I've washed them.

What Kind of Baby Is She?

The clinging baby The endless stream of people bursting with unwanted advice for you will probably recommend leaving the baby to toughen her up, 'and make her more independent'. All that this will do is change your baby from being unhappy to be away from you to being thoroughly suspicious every time you leave the room in case you are going to dump her again with someone she doesn't really want to spend time with.

My mother was convinced that I was a clinging child and practised many of these techniques in a million futile attempts to make me less Mummy fixated. All that happened was that I became a child who could have clung for Britain in the 1965 Olympic Games, reaching a high point when I would lie prone along the crack of the door to the bathroom in case she was making her getaway through the toilet window.

Mothers who push their children away from them and reject their babies' natural inclination to be with them all the time, something babies are programmed to do, are more likely to be the ones 'making a rod for their own backs'. Try to enjoy the togetherness: unless she is very used to the person or you absolutely have to, it's best never to leave your little baby with anyone else. The babies who feel confident that their mothers are near by are always the ones who feel confident enough to strike out on their own, returning to base for a cuddle occasionally to recharge their batteries before making another foray into the big world.

The children who are really clinging are often the ones who have had to deal with unwanted separation from their mothers when they were babies. They have been forced into independence before they were ready for it. What we have to try and solve for ourselves is the problem of carrying on with our lives without excluding our children, and treating them as a cumbersome appendage we long to get away from. Then the battle we invent between ourselves and our babies would vanish.

A child is independent sooner than anyone can imagine: that fragrant stage of being inseparable won't last for long, and it seems a pity not to enjoy it the way we enjoy all the other stages of our baby's development into a young child.

The good baby I hate to say this, but often a 'good' baby is really a bored baby in disguise! Many parents boast that they can leave their baby playing happily on the floor, and return some time later and still find her playing quietly there. Although this is an excellent way of finding time to wash up, it is not the best plan for stimulating your baby into early speech or reading, or even savouring time together playing and learning, or paying a trip to the park, which even young babies thoroughly enjoy. Some of these parents are glad that they have a quiet baby, and an under-stimulated baby suits them because she isn't demanding.

A thoroughly villainous baby, the sort who wrecks rooms as she investigates her surroundings, and pulls everything over in her search for new things to play with, may be exhausting, but as long as you've baby-proofed your home, her behaviour is to be welcomed. Later on she will turn into the most entertaining companion, having forced you to give her the attention she needed. In both human and animal studies, there is firm evidence that it is active experience rather than passive (such as TV watching) that most benefits the young.

So it's wise to check next time your baby seems either grumpy without reason or simply unduly quiet that she is not actually just thoroughly fed up.

The gifted baby She will be extra curious about everything going on around her, will explore the home and her possessions with her hands and mouth, and, once she can crawl, be into everything. Often gifted children do not sleep as well as other babies – although bear in mind that it might mean that your baby has roaring colic rather than she's a genius. She may also cry more, simply because she feels bored and wants you to chat, read or play with her. Gifted children get cross and frustrated at their own limitations.

If you do think that your child is a gifted one, and I'm sure there are only about two mothers reading this who haven't already recognised their baby immediately – all you can do is be there to help her stretch herself, and bombard her with the special stimulation she needs.

Playing and Learning With Your Baby Einstein

For all babies, learning is fun. In fact, for most babies, nearly everything is fun and they are constantly in the midst of the excitement of discovering new things. One of the ways they acquire skills is through playing with you. You should never feel stupid playing rather silly baby games, as most of them have a real purpose for the baby, as well as being fun for both of you. As I have already stressed, talking to your baby, along with endless cuddling, is one of the most important activities of those early weeks. She will start to make noises and different sounds and then we take *our* turn. While maintaining eye contact, these are the first steps towards conversation. Watch another mother playing with her baby and you will notice that she often asks her questions, and always waits for a reply.

Toys By eight weeks your baby will have started to grab at her toys and will particularly like mobiles and rattles, musical toys, activity centres, and I have found that mirrors are also a winner. Babies need a lot of practice, as they are trying to grasp so many ideas at once, so they particularly like very repetitive games such as peek-a-boo. They will soon get bored with the same old rattle. If you use your imagination, you and your older children can make some yourself, as an activity on a wet afternoon. Cotton reels tied together rattle furiously when banged.

Babies also enjoy playing hiding games. Hiding a ticking alarm clock under one of several upturned shoe boxes is a good one. And of course, there is that old standby, the wooden box for banging on with a wooden spoon. Alternatively, a biscuit tin with a spoon makes an interesting chiming sound the first 300 times.

From about six months onwards, your baby will probably start to show an interest in balls, the soft ones, and the hard ones with something inside the see-through plastic. Bath toys will be a wow, and also the baby walker and bouncer. Any stacking toys, bricks and push-along animals or trucks will be popular.

She will also feel ready to tackle the mysteries of the lift-out jigsaw, the kind with knobs attached to the bits, and another picture lurking underneath. You will be astonished!

Books for babies It is *never* too early to start reading with your baby. Even a weeny little baby will take an interest in a colourful book, and love getting close with you to look at the pictures. Try starting your baby with those cardboard books full of vivid pictures and photos of all the things that are becoming familiar to her, and repeating the words to go with them. Then a little later the two of you can move on to 'lift-the-flap' books that six-month-old babies seem to adore. A little later you'll find that picture stories are wildly entertaining, especially the ones which feature children with their baby brothers and sisters discovering the world around them.

Don't let people laugh at you for introducing reading early. It is such a pleasure to look at books together and your baby will learn a great deal. If you feel ambitious, you might also invest in a copy of Glen Doman's *Teach Your Baby to Read* which is a simple but effective teaching technique for babies of about one upwards – and it's great fun to try.

Baby Exercise

Children today are considerably fatter than youngsters were in the mid-Sixties, and a recent survey in America claimed that their heart-lung fitness lagged behind that of most middle-aged joggers. Among the junior school children who were studied, 98 per cent of them showed at least one major risk factor in the development of heart disease. On average the children studied spent only 1 per cent of their day doing an activity that significantly increased their heart rate. Even when I was young, school sports were an almost daily, if utterly loathed, activity, and they did keep us fit. Now, since most schools offer limited PE, parents are becoming increasingly concerned about how they can supplement their child's exercise activities.

Starting them young If you begin by massaging your newborn baby and introducing her to swimming by the time she's three months old, you will have given her a head start with the exercise habit. By the twelfth to sixteenth week, infants naturally start to push against their feet, reflexively building their leg muscles. By their second six months, babies will be able to move over obstacles. This is a good time to start all those games of tickling, and crawling over cushions and other obstacle-race manoeuvres. By two years old, toddlers will be able to join organisations like Tumble Tots, which teach elementary gymnastic skills.

Remember that babies will pick up the exercise habit best by watching you. If you are exercising, she will soon jump in and try to copy you. Once children are three years old, they can be introduced to actual sports.

Other benefits Gymnastic training for babies and toddlers helps with their cognitive skill development. A thirteen-month-old baby who has learned to do a somersault has learned to think in a logical sequence which involves reasoning – excellent training for the brain.

Eating Out Together

This is an experience that can make strong men quiver in their Calvin Klein underpants. It is only equalled by eating out with a toddler ... Babies (unless they are very small and lying beaming in your arms) find it almost *impossible* to sit still in any kind of café. You either let them move about, in which case they throw plates on to the floor and juggle with the cutlery, crawl over to fellow diners and stuff strands of spaghetti in their faces, or they go wild with frustration at being stuck on your lap and make themselves go rigid, especially if they wanted three portions of lobster thermidor and not semolina pudding with jam.

It is a good idea, if you can cope with these early traumatic experiences in cafés and restaurants, to take your baby out for a snack frequently so that she gets used to it. This will also mean a lot less work when she's a toddler and really able to demolish the place singlehandedly in the space of time it takes to take out a baby wipe.

This is not to say that I blame babies. In this country babies are not welcomed with wide open arms into restaurants, and sensible facilities like highchairs and bibs are all too rare (unlike the Continent or America). In England restaurateurs assume a look on their faces like someone recently mummified by an amateur if you dare to walk over their threshold carrying a baby, and other diners dive for the menu, terrified that you're going to start breast-feeding or that the baby might throw up.

It makes sense to *be prepared* as you would be on any expedition with a baby. Pack a bottle, a bib, a packet of wipes, and pick a time when the baby isn't shattered. If your baby does get upset, take her outside for a little walk to calm her down. *Don't* be put off by the hostile looks of those who consider your baby to be an alien: sit with your back to them – it's their loss not to be able to see a cute little baby while they eat.

On the Road

The idea of taking a baby on a bus is traumatic enough in the early weeks, but by now you will be feeling more confident and even braving the train or the aeroplane. Speaking as one who travels long distances with small children often, I have one piece of golden advice: let your baby *sleep* when she's travelling. All the horror stories we hear of babies screaming on planes and trains are stories about babies who aren't given the chance to nap. Screaming babies are exhausted babies. Just cuddle your baby close on the plane or train or touring bus, and she'll fall happily asleep and not get wilder and wilder with excitement and lack of sleep. The other general rule is always carry a clean change of clothes for you and the baby, even if it's just a T-shirt and track suit pants each, as there's nothing worse than arriving at your destination covered with poo and puke.

For any journey with a baby you must take a survival kit, and keep it with you at all times. If your baby's still bottle-feeding, take a large bottle of boiled water and the milk powder and mix the feeds as you need them. Loads of ready-made feeds will get too warm and not be safe. Don't forget nappies, a disposable bag for dirty nappies (preferably the scented kind), bibs, and a feeding bottle of sterilised water for a thirsty baby. If your baby's on solids, take plenty of food, such as tiny sandwiches, baby rice, fruit. And remember to take a good supply of baby wipes – the lotion kind rather than the scented ones as these tend to dry the skin.

In the car Every year thousands of children under the age of thirteen are killed in cars, and thousands upon thousands more are injured. Never carry your baby in the front seat, as you will crush her to death when you fall forwards on to her if the car has to stop suddenly. Up until six months a baby should be strapped securely in her carry-cot in the back seat, and after that safely strapped into a car seat.

There are many different sorts of baby car seats available, but you should only buy one that has the BSI kite mark of safety. It is a professional job to get your baby car seat fitted into the car properly, but it isn't expensive, and the consequences of not having one are truly too horrific to contemplate. So remember ALWAYS to use the car seat every single trip, no matter how short it is.

Two other things are worth mentioning: in warm weather any baby left in a car can get seriously dehydrated: and with the increase of baby snatches it doesn't seem wise to leave your baby anywhere unsupervised for even a minute.

You can buy specially designed car sunscreen blinds for babies, which fasten to the window with suction pads and cut out glaring sunlight on little faces.

If you're going to be doing a lot of car travel with your baby, it's a good idea to check with your GP for help with travel sickness. Sometimes these days it's simply a question of putting an elastic band round the wrist. Keep the windows of the car open, drive at a steady pace without jerking the brakes on and off, and take regular stops so that your baby can have some fresh air.

Going abroad The first thing that you have to do when booking a holiday is find out exactly what the real facts are from your travel agent. If the place you're planning to book offers babysitting, find out if that means a telephone listening service, a rep occasionally passing the door (which isn't good enough) or someone actually sitting in the room. In many hotels, members of the staff do babysitting but it can be expensive. Personally, I'd imagine you'd be barking mad to leave a baby with someone neither of you knows or trusts. The next thing to do is find out about cot facilities (if you use a cot). Some foreign cots don't actually meet British safety standards, so you should consider taking a small, foldaway travel cot. These can be hired, as well. When looking at glamorous brochures, parents should keep an eye open for safety hazards such as busy roads, plate glass doors and lots of steps to the swimming pool.

Having booked your holiday, the next thing to do is get insurance. Your own household policy may cover you for some aspects of your travel, but you need to check out exactly what. Medical insurance is one of those things that if you don't need it when you're on holiday it seems like a complete waste of money, but you can be sure if that you don't have it (because you haven't needed it the last five times) then your child will develop measles the first day in Majorca, and may well have broken her leg on the way to the GP.

The next thing to do is get your sprog a passport. Many parents have their children added to their passport. For purely sentimental reasons, I don't think this is a good idea. There are few cuter things in the world than a baby's first passport, complete with an adorable photograph of said baby clutching cuddly toy. It takes eight weeks for a postal application to the passport office in Petty France, London – but you can call in person, although there is usually a long queue. You get an application form from a travel agent or a main post office – and don't panic if you haven't got one yet; you can get a British Visitors passport from main post offices from Monday to Friday (although this won't get you into certain countries, including America).

If you're going very far afield, you'll need to get everyone immunised. Polio is still a problem in parts of Southern Europe, and it is important to be protected from tetanus. Be sure to ask your GP what your baby will need.

Packing for a hot country Do not forget that your baby will need extra drinks in the heat, so pack large amounts of disposable bottles. A car seat is also absolutely essential if you are planning to hire a car. Both Hertz and Avis will fit a child's car seat in advance if you contact them in good time. If you can't arrange this, it is imperative to take your own with you – even at risk of looking like a travelling circus when you arrive at the airport.

You must pack a very basic first aid kit for your child. This should include a very powerful, waterproof sunscreen that doesn't wash off in water. Toddlers and babies should never be exposed directly to the sun at all, but can bask naked in the shade. Toddlers will invariably want to play, but as long as they're wearing sunscreen and a sunhat, that's fine – except during the extremely strong sunlight of the midday hours. It's wise also to pack lots of baggy T-shirts for them to run around in and swim in, for added protection.

Also in your first aid kit, include antiseptic and plasters, and a bottle of Calpol for other ailments. And finally, it might be a good idea to buy a special buzzer that keeps mosquitoes away from babies at night. Alternatively, douse them with a suitable repellant. Your chemist will be able to recommend one.

There are certain special baby products you may not be able to buy abroad. You'll be able to buy nappies, of course, but you'll find that European ones are less absorbent than their British or American counterparts. You may be able to find your usual brand of baby formula but though it may bear the same name the ingredients will not necessarily be the same. I would definitely recommend taking the formula with you, as any change will upset your baby considerably, even if it means you can't fit your sequinned evening gowns into your suitcase. When you're mixing up the formula once you're there, don't forget to boil all the mineral water you put into the baby's bottle. If you must use manufactured baby food, you'll be able to find major brands, but there won't be a lot of choice and you may want to take your baby's favourite with you. Of course, you could try not using them at all, which, as I have said, is considerably easier.

On the plane It's wise to try and get a flight that doesn't leave very late at night. Night flights are very disruptive for young children and it's often possible to find another company that's going to the same place at a more civilised time. I would definitely prefer to go early morning with a baby than late at night. On a chartered flight, there are no special facilities for little ones – for example, they won't have nappies on board, nor will they have any special foods, and it will probably all seem very crowded. And because your under-two will be travelling free, she isn't even entitled to a seat. So on a charter flight try to get the seats in the first row that face the bulkhead, where there's much more leg room.

Once Fifi got to be a slightly bigger baby, that is, not needing to be

172

held all the time, I used to make her a little bed on the floor under my legs. Which meant that she was able to stretch out, rather than having to sleep rolled in a ball. It's always worth asking the stewardess if the plane's carrying any sky cots, which are small carry-cots that fit on to your foldaway table. On some airlines, you may even be allowed to take your own carry-cot on board, and it's always worth trying to insist as much as you can, rather than backing down immediately on these points. You are not there to be polite to airport staff; you are there to ensure that your baby has a pleasant flight.

If you are worried about breast-feeding with a large audience of Club 18–30 aficionados, get a seat next to a window with a member of your family sitting next to you, which will give you adequate protection as long as you don't wear difficult clothes. The air stewardesses will warm up your bottles and also put any bottles you wish to keep cold in their fridge. They can also supply boiling water for feeds, if you run out.

During take-off and landing, some babies cry. If your baby has not flown before, be sure that you keep her calm beforehand. A drink, which encourages swallowing, definitely eases the pressure in her ears. Alternatively, give your baby a dummy.

Making Your Home Safety Proof

All babies will at some point have accidents like falling down the stairs or slipping in the bath. But you can prevent much by taking various precautions.

Floors It's a good idea to put a non-slip backing on your rugs, and make sure that floor tiles are actually lying flat. If you are planning to re-tile a floor, avoid highly glazed tiles. In the bath, put a large rubber mat to prevent bathtime skids.

Stairs My children have always regarded our stairs as some sort of indoor adventure playground. Only yesterday I came home to find Fifi actually hanging from the top banister with her legs dangling close to the ceiling lamp on the landing below. So it's a good idea to use a safety gate or a barrier to stop access up or down – although safety gates don't actually stop older children climbing *over*. But they are still a good idea for anywhere that's vaguely dangerous – at the top or bottom of the stairs, across a back door or at the threshold of a garage or potting shed.

Make sure that there's no room for your baby to climb through the banisters, and all parents with horizontal banisters should net or board them up immediately, as the temptation to use them as ladders will be irresistible to toddlers. Always keep your stairs free from shoes or coats. A single toy can trip you and cause a serious accident if you are coming downstairs holding a child. Be careful if your baby uses her baby walker upstairs. Babies have fallen downstairs while trapped in these contraptions and suffered serious injuries.

While on the subject of heights, balconies are extremely dangerous places. Balconies should always be netted or boarded up, and beware of large tables, pot plants or garden chairs that can be climbed on and fallen off over the edge. Never leave your baby on a balcony without you.

Windows Check that your windows can't be opened too wide. Child-proof safety catches should be fitted, and should also always be put on upstairs windows. These can be bought at DIY and hardware stores. If you have large, plate glass windows or sliding doors, decorate them with stickers so that they become obvious. It's important to make sure that children understand that they shouldn't run or play near glass doors. If you are putting your doors in yourself, fit safety glass.

Furniture Never, ever, leave a baby unattended for a second on tables or beds. Babies learn to roll off everything very early. One minute they can't do it, and the next minute they can. If you must move away from your child, either take her with you or put her down on the floor on a cushion. Check that your furniture will withstand bumps and tugs when your baby is learning to walk, and that it won't fall over if bumped into with a baby walker. Harnesses are extremely useful, not only to stop babies rolling off things, but also in supermarket trolleys and other seats.

Play it Safe – A Guide to Preventing Children's Accidents, Health Education Authority. Available free from *Play It Safe*, Department HS2, 39 Standard Road, London NW10 6HD.

Hot and Bothered: What to Do When Your Baby's Ill

It is notoriously difficult not to panic if your baby seems ill. My father agrees thoroughly with me about this as he was one of the world's championship panickers. When I was small, I fell straight through our cucumber frames, cutting my leg open. My father was in the bathroom innocently washing a pair of Y-fronts when I raced in pouring with blood and shrieking. Calmly he removed his half-clean underpants from the sink and wrapped them around my leg. When the doctor was finally summoned to have a look at the healing scar, it transpired that my father's underpants had actually grown into my leg, so a further hospital drama was needed to rip them out again. I can sympathise with my father's plight, though: the combination of blood, shrieking, and instant panic is enough to send anyone's elementary first aid straight out of the window.

I can't say enough that if there is *anything* wrong with your baby – if she seems miserable, sleepless, fractious, or feverish – it is wise to call the doctor, no matter how foolish you feel or, if you are unlucky, how foolish you can be made to feel by some doctor's assistants. With babies the most innocent little problems do have a frightening way of escalating if left unchecked – a little redness around the tummy button can turn into an infection which turns into projectile vomiting and a high fever. It can be a scary chain of events for any mother and is easily solved by getting the doctor to check your child early.

A few weeks ago my baby got a high temperature, and the doctor came round and told us there was nothing wrong. As soon as his black bag had whisked around the front door I was as purple in the face as Peaches, howling so loudly that the windows shook and the baby gazed up at me in silent wonder at the racket. 'She's got a terminal disease and he's not telling us,' I shrieked at my husband, who was still standing nonplussed clutching half a Junior Paracetamol and a cup of Appletize for the baby. He handed them over to me.

I repeat this small tale simply because I know how difficult it is to be calm when someone weeny is ill and you don't quite know what it is that's wrong. NEVER HESITATE TO CALL YOUR DOCTOR. And remember, every mother worries about her baby: there'd be something wrong if she didn't.

Temperatures When a baby gets a temperature, it can happen very suddenly and unexpectedly and is more than likely to run higher than an adult's, as the temperature-regulating mechanism in a baby doesn't work as well. You should immediately call the doctor.

Your baby definitely has a fever if her temperature is over 100 degrees Fahrenheit (37.7 degrees Centigrade). This will make her look flushed, and her skin will be hot to the touch. She will become unusually quiet, drowsy, or even delirious. Some babies can seem fairly well despite a very high temperature – and conversely, just to confuse you totally, could be quite poorly with a normal one.

You should definitely ring your GP if your baby has a convulsion or has ever had one in the past. In some children, a fever can trigger an epileptic-type fit known as a febrile convulsion. After the fit, the baby will probably fall asleep. You should cool her as quickly as possible with small, damp sponges. Stay with her, roll her on to her side so she can breathe, and do not try to restrain her or force anything into her mouth.

Other times you should ring your doctor are when the baby has a temperature over 102 degrees Fahrenheit (39 degrees Centigrade) accompanied by a headache or a stiff neck (which can be a sign of meningitis); if she is delirious; if the fever has lasted more than twenty-four hours; if she has had a temperature and diarrhoea for more than twenty-four hours.

There are things that you can do to lower your baby's temperature. It is usually possible with a combination of the following: medicine such as a paracetamol syrup like Calpol. Doses vary according to the child's age and are shown on the bottle or packet. *Never give aspirin* or any medicine containing aspirin to a child under twelve, as this can trigger a serious reaction. Encourage your baby to drink a lot of water – fever can cause dehydration because of all the sweating. Keep rehydrating crystals (Rehidrat or Dioralyte) in the first aid box. A breast-fed child can have rehydrating fluid as well as breast milk. If you're bottle-feeding, substitute the fluid for bottle milk for twenty-four hours. A dehydrated baby is often very quiet and apathetic.

Holding your baby constantly, close to your chest, has a soothing effect that will help her get the rest she needs.

Finally, if she is still hot, remove all of her clothing down to the nappy, remove most of the bedclothes, slightly open the window and place a cool, wet facecloth on her forehead. If her temperature continues, you can sponge her body with lukewarm water. Do not use cold water, as this causes the body to try and reduce heat loss. You may find that her skin is hypersensitive, and sponging may even hurt. If this is so, and if you have a fan, you can direct it into the room – but not on to the baby. It's important to try and cover your anxieties as much as possible, as a baby will always be affected by your mood.

Snot, snot and more snot Any baby who has a cold should see a doctor immediately, because colds can often lead to ear infections, which in turn can lead to perforations of the eardrum.

Sore ears My daughter Peaches has suffered from sore ears since she was a weeny little thing. The merest tug on the earlobe is enough to send me racing for the telephone to call out the doctor. And while my doctor assures me that many children are plagued with almost continuous troubles with their delicate ears, this isn't a huge comfort. He also tells me never to feel badly about calling him out, as ear infection can be very very dangerous for a baby's hearing if left untreated. As with most childhood ailments, you will get better and better at spotting the warning signals. Tearfulness and crankiness a couple of days in advance are often the first signs of worse to follow.

The best treatment I've found for a sore ear is lots of cuddles, a carefully measured dose of Junior Paracetamol, and a well-covered hot water bottle close to the affected area until Doctor arrives in a hail of screeching sirens.

There are many causes of sore ears in babies – new teeth coming, a sore throat, glue ear, cold wind, inflammations of the eardrum – all of these can result in a horrid throbbing ear that makes a baby's day and night a misery of pain.

Throwing up This is always alarming, but not necessarily serious. Has your baby had too much milk? Maybe she is just overflowing. If she seems quite well, and just pukes up a little bit of feed, don't panic. However, if your baby does forceful, projectile vomiting that shoots milk right away from her (and often all over your new wallpaper), see your doctor.

Is your baby sick every time she lies down? Sometimes this means that the valve which should be keeping food down hasn't developed properly yet. Again, see your doctor, who may advise sitting your baby in a sloping chair after meals.

Sometimes, babies start vomiting if you change their milk formula or introduce cereals. The vomiting could be a food allergy and you should see your doctor.

If vomiting starts suddenly and is accompanied by diarrhoea, it could be caused by a virus. You should see your doctor, as this can lead to dehydration. Her fontanelle (the soft spot on the top of her head) may have sunk in, and if you pinch up a bit of skin, instead of returning at once, the crease only slowly goes back to shape, like an old person's skin. These are all warning signals. Vomiting is very often a sign of an infection lurking elsewhere, such as the throat or ears or even the belly button.

Have you got the needle about vaccinations? Most mothers get extremely worried about vaccinations, even though immunisation has virtually removed the danger of most killer diseases in children. When my daughter went for her first injection, my mother rang up from France with a litany of tales about relations who had been turned into vegetables by their jabs. Not only do you have to sit in the surgery while the doctor sticks a needle into the most beautiful baby in the history of Western civilisation, you are also remembering what seems like a tidal wave of publicity about the small minority of children who do suffer from serious side-effects. But at the same time, these injections are protecting your child against diptheria, polio, tetanus and whooping cough, all of which used to kill children.

Doctors will advise you not to take your baby for any of her injections if at the same time she is suffering from a temperature or feeling unwell. A baby who has suffered from brain damage at birth, or one who has fits or has suffered a severe reaction to a prior injection, shouldn't have the whooping cough vaccine, or the measles injection. If she is suffering from egg allergy she should not be immunised against measles until her allergy has disappeared. Epilepsy in a parent or sibling is another reason why the whooping cough vaccination should not be given.

Immunisation starts at three to four months for the first triple (diptheria, tetanus and whooping cough) plus polio. A second triple is given at five to six months and a third at ten months. At thirteen months your baby will be immunised against measles, after which a triple and polio booster is given at four and a half years. At eleven, girls will be given the Rubella injection, and at twelve both boys and girls are immunised against TB.

After her injections, your baby may be miserable and hot. Her arm is likely to be sore, and with my children, a small, hard lump developed on the arm which took some days to disappear.

MOTHERS AND WORK

Having It All?

A lot of theorising goes on about the pros and cons of working once you're a mother, much of it backed up by statistics and claims of proof. In the end, it boils down to how the mother herself *feels*, so this is an unashamedly personal view.

When you decide to have a child, it's not a whim of the moment, it is a commitment that will last many years. If you think you can give birth to another human being and skip back to work in a matter of weeks, you are being at best irresponsible and at worst, selfish. Of course there are some mothers who will be able to return to work without any guilt – which is fine for them, but miserable for the baby. You cannot be a biological mother only. The very word embodies all those things we believe to be essential: nurturing, care, teaching, kindness. To deprive a baby of these is to stunt her growth, both physically and mentally. We have been seduced by the glossy magazine ethic of 'having it all'. It is a great lie. It has caused women untold misery and generated a million guilt-ridden insecurities. No one can have it all; nobody ever does.

Economic independence is less of an issue here than the fact that a lot of women simply do not want to stay at home with children. They work not so much for the pay as for the social aspect: the friends and the camaraderie. They feel that their brains will go numb from the relentless drudgery of child-rearing, and that their innate worth and talent will go to waste. They don't want to be removed from society, trapped and bored by the apparently low intellectual level of child-rearing. But all jobs are essentially boring. You do not fulfil your life-role by being employed by someone else to do a job that in the end is as inessential as the next one. There are a thousand people who can do your job as well or better and that is the ego-crushing reality. We are not all power-suited-briefcase-carrying-decising-mak-ing beauties. On the whole, we are like men, doing pedestrian office work, factory chores, shop work, manual labour. Hardly glamorous. The price of a pay packet is the dull ritual of a non-fulfilling drone-like grind. This is freedom? This is any different from the supposed bore-dom of raising your child?

It seems obvious to me that there is a clear stark choice: to have a career until such time as your desire for children overrides your desire for work. At which point you quit your job, perhaps to pick it up again later. Or the converse, you have your children now, wait until they've grown, then begin your work outside the home. But if you want children simultaneously and *now*, if you 'want it all', if you want that curse of our age, self-gratification immediately – forget it. The crude fact is children are a career: accept it or feel guilty.

Once your baby reaches school age, then part-time work might be feasible, as long as it is carried out at no cost to your child. Best of all, work part-time at home, if this is at all possible. Supposedly, with increased telecommunications, we shall all be able to do this. However, this assumes that we are all lawyers, authors, accountants etc. It's pretty impossible to work at home as a hairdresser, no matter how many computers you have. The argument will be that there's no difference between working at home and working outside – you're still occupied by work. But this is disingenuous, a child is still aware of your presence, and can interrupt when she wants to, can play around you and talk to you. If you can do this at your workplace, then fantastic, but it is even better in a familiar environment with all its comforts and securities. The introduction of flexitime will become the norm over the next decade or so, which is to be welcomed if it means women with school-age children can work but still lead a full home life.

Somehow we've arrived at a point in our civilised development where babies are an optional extra to be picked up during 'quality time' like the family dog. For the baby who sees her mother for twenty minutes in the day, this time is no doubt precious – but it is not enough. For the career woman, it is a great conscience salver. Some Californian child-care guru has approved her lifestyle with quasi-scientific theories, and this eases the residual guilt and mitigates the indifference.

If you are going to feel guilty, stay home. If you are indifferent to children, don't have them. Babies NEED their mothers.

There are so many child-care theories one begins to think of babies

as entirely abstract things. They are humans. They are undefended, tiny animals who are purely instinctual. They have no weapons against the culture or intellect of adults. When you apply your theories to them, they have the nauseatingly human habit of disproving them.

No political theory ever worked as it should, no economic theory has ever been proved. No child-care theory has ever been devised that most experienced women could not have come up with. Motherhood can never be conditional. It can never be like the modern marriage which, if proving unsatisfactory, can be set aside for something or someone else. It can never be a 'lifestyle' where, once picked up, can be dropped again upon being found wanting.

Children need their mothers. It is so obvious a thing to say it sounds ludicrous, and yet the very assertion known and understood in its most visceral, basic sense to all animals will probably create a furore at least privately in the minds of many women reading this. If given the choice between the imagined self-fulfilment of an individual and the mental health of a well-adjusted child, I'd choose the latter, for all our sakes.

Why not let men do the mothering? The argument is so fatuous and banal it deserves the banality of the response: because they are men. If in the 100,000 years of human development men had taken over the traditional feminine role, I would say yes, why not? If you suggest that we have changed men so radically over the past twenty years that they now go completely against type, culture and tradition, then you are deluded. The 'new man', like the glamorous career woman, is an invention of an industry which feeds on the insecurities of women, and when finding none invents new ones.

For single mothers who have no choice, there are no easy answers. But I would venture (and it is easy for me to speak) that, if you can possibly afford to, you should stay at home with your baby (and society should take measures to ensure that you can).

I have absolutely no desire to 'drive women back into the home'. But even that over-used expression is so laden with white-hot rhetorical language that it is impossible to use it without stirring passions. Women can go in and out of the home on revolving doors for all I care. There is no shame in being a housewife; the pleasure and fulfilment this role gives some women is no less valuable than the fulfilment of working outside the home. I will scream if I hear 'I'm just a housewife' or 'Only a housewife, I'm afraid' again.

If you choose to stay at home with your baby, then you have chosen to put her emotional well-being before that demon of our times, the idea of instant self-gratification. For women who want to work, who wish to be fulfilled by it, who wish their talents to be tested, who want the material freedom their earnings will bring, every opportunity should be given to them, and every encouragement. Women who want children, likewise. The women who want both simultaneously are going to be unhappy. For your baby's sake, look after her – she needs *you*.

Rights and Benefits

Once you discover you're pregnant, you have some basic rights at work, as long as you are fit, and don't have a history of miscarriage. Many women choose to continue working; it stops them lying around watching themselves expand day after day. Most pregnant women have given up full-time work by week twenty-eight.

Rights You are legally entitled to paid time off to attend antenatal appointments. You have the right to stay in your job, unless it is considered unsuitable for a pregnant women, in which case the employer is obliged to provide you with alternative employment.

In order to have the right to return to work after the baby is born, you must have been in your job at least two years, and have worked a minimum of sixteen hours per week. Three weeks before you leave, write to your employer stating your intention to return. Your employer will write to you after the birth to find out if you still want to return. This is your chance to say no thanks! If you say yes, you must inform your employer at least three weeks in advance of your return date.

Benefits You must have been with your employer a minimum of two years (full-time) or five years (part-time), and have been paying National Insurance, in order to receive Statutory Maternity Pay. You must also continue working until week twenty-six of pregnancy.

If you are not eligible for this, you may be able to claim Maternity Allowance, paid by the DSS. In this case, you must have been paying National Insurance for at least six months of the year that ends when you're six months pregant.

Your local *Citizens Advice Bureau* is a good source of advice and information.

Alternatives for Working Mothers

Penelope Leach had noted that, 'Our society is very unchild-centred across the board. Parents in this country have always been forced to keep parenthood quite quiet. Indeed, the government sees us as a nation of workers who rather tiresomely have other concerns which get in the way. Possession of a child or two is simply not relevant.'

Short-term maternity leave forces companies and employers to realise that pregnancy and family life are facts. Everyone would agree that leave ought to be automatic for men and women, but recently Martin Allen, a footballer with Queen's Park Rangers, was fined two weeks' pay for leaving his team to be present at the birth of his son.

For women who are forced by circumstances to *have* to leave their homes and find work, to talk of the tragedy of the babies left at home must seem both smug and horribly complacent – but there are glimmerings of hope on the horizon as alternatives to conventional working practices become possible.

Working from home In America, many companies are letting employees whose jobs are suitable work from home. You might think about trying to persuade your employer to let you do this, once you've become a mother. You will then be able to tailor your work to your domestic schedule so much more easily.

Obviously, it won't be easy to talk your employer into this, but it will help if you have a clear idea in your mind of what your company wants from you. Jobs done on a project-by-project basis, law work, writing, anything artistic or creative, sewing, accounting, computer or telephone work can all be done from home.

Working from home means you make all your own rules; there is no travelling to and from work each day; you'll be with your baby and be feeling no guilt. And you won't have to dress up or indulge in office politics – you'll just get on with the job.

However, you may feel isolated at times. Because you don't leave work at the end of the day, it's always there at home. The atmosphere at home isn't very professional – your baby will cry at inopportune moments and the doorbell will keep ringing. You'll need help in the house for the times when you really have to work hard without interruption – but you'll have the comfort of being at hand if anyone wants you, for however trivial a matter – a quick cuddle, for example.

Keytime Working nine to five, five days a week, is impossible for most mothers of young babies. The Midland Bank now offers 'keytime' where working hours are reduced but the important work gets done.

Flexitime This allows employees to choose their hours, as long as they work a certain number of hours in a week.

Part-time work This is still, sadly, regarded by many as low-status work, but you may discover that you can work part-time from home. I have one friend who has become a successful collagist working from home; another does business lunches in the hours that suit her.

Job-sharing This is on the increase, especially in local authorities and the voluntary sector. Two mothers can share one job, each working part-time at full-time! Between them they retain benefits such as sick leave and pensions. Unfortunately, this has yet to be adopted by larger companies.

Mother Substitutes

Ideally, all children would stay with their mothers for at least the first three years of their lives. If you have decided that this is not to be, then there are certain things you should strive for for your child's happiness and security away from you.

The first one is continuity of care. Babies need to have one special person looking after them, with whom they can build a warm and loving relationship, not a constant stream of new faces all doing things differently. This can lead to a great many behavioural problems later on, and children will find it harder to maintain stable, close relationships.

You have to find out – almost like MI5 – about the nanny or child minder you are employing. Your baby won't be able to tell you what she's like when you are not there, so it's up to you to find out if she plays with your baby and chats to her, and does all those little special things with her that you would do if you were together. It's really important to find out from people who are likely to see them together what the nanny or childminder is like. Sometimes a working mother is so worried about maintaining continuity that she can find herself ignoring warning signs that the baby is unhappy with the care she is given in her absence.

Which brings me to the hardest thing of all: many mothers would rather give up work and come home than realise that, although they will always be MUMMY and special, the baby has become attached to her minder. This is only to be expected, yet it is often ignored by 'experts' in an effort to make women feel better about working away from home for very long hours. But the horrible old cliché of the baby falling over and running to her nanny or childminder has more than a ring of truth, and is terribly painful to a mother.

Often babies protest loudly about being left, but, as they realise that this is doing them no good, they adapt to the circumstances. They can even seem to be rejecting the mother as a punishment for deserting them.

A good childminder A proper childminder is someone who is registered by the local authority to look after children in her own home, and often does so with her own children there, too.

Although this is the cheapest form of child care, it's wise to be aware of the pitfalls. The first is that if the childminder has her own children there, your baby, however young, may start to feel like a second-class citizen. You may be thinking that it will be fun for her to be with other youngsters, but babies need a loving mother substitute, first and foremost; playing with chums is very secondary to this and will be for a long time.

You need to make sure that you *like* the childminder – she will be spending a lot of time with your baby, out of the baby's home surroundings, and will be influencing how she is growing up a lot more than you at first imagine. You need to know as much as you can about the set-up she runs; what food will she provide? What play? Naps? Trips outside to parks?

A good nanny She is someone who will live-in with you, and not drive you around the bend. She will love your children enormously, and take great care to stimulate them and teach them all the things you'd be teaching them if you were around all the time. She should, in a perfect world, stay with you as long as you can manage to hold on to her, and it is better for the baby if your nanny becomes a real part of your family, not just someone you 'pay' to look after her, but someone who's a friend who lives with you all and has fun with you all. All this 'not eating with the nanny' stuff doesn't work, and in the long term makes everyone unhappy and uncomfortable.

It's hard to find the right nanny, as so many young girls only want to do it for a little while, but if you find one that suits you I'd recommend doing as much as you can to make her happy so that she'll stay – and ensure that vital continuity of care.

Crèche and nursery Proper registered crèches are run the same way that local authority day nurseries are – and there are strict regulations about numbers, hygiene, and cooking facilities. But there are still relatively few nurseries and crèches and so the demand for places is very competitive.

If your baby is going to be taken each day to a crèche or nursery, it would be best if just one person looked after her. The great drawback is that because of illness, holidays, a high turnover of staff, your baby can become thoroughly confused and depressed. Different people caring for her each day will not make for security. But on the other hand, there are babies with gregarious personalities who will make satisfactory progress in a well-run, stable crèche where the children are both entertained, soothed and stimulated.

You need to ask the staff how your baby seems while you are away from her. If she is withdrawn and cries a great deal, you may have to consider the financial burden of getting her one-to-one care in your own home, on her own territory. Make sure that you get a true answer, as there is a great tendency to tell mothers anything to keep them happy.

Working Mothers' Association, 23 Webbs Road, London SW11 6RU (071 228 3757).
National Childminding Association, 8 Mason's Hill, Bromley, Kent BR2 9EY (081 464 6164).
National Council for One-Parent Families, 255 Kentish Town Road, London NW5 2LX (071 267 1361).

A NOTE ON THE AUTHOR

Paula Yates has published several books, and written for *Elle, Cosmopolitan*, the *Observer* and the *Sunday Times*. She has also appeared on more than thirty magazine covers. Her television career includes *The Tube*, and the series *BabyBaby*. In 1985 and 1986 she won the Gold Award from the New York Film and Television Festival for the best documentary interview. She is married, has almost three children, and lives in Kent and London where she does all her work during naptimes – the children's, not hers. Her favourite occupation is lying in the long grass with the children eating fig rolls.